Geologic Wonders
Of
West Texas

By

Donald P. McGookey

Published by Donald P. McGookey
12607 Pine Warbler
San Antonio,TX 78253

First Edition, 2004
Second Printing, 2006
Third Printing 2013

For ordering Information Contact:

Donald P. McGookey
12607 Pine Warbler
San Antonio, TX 78253
432 230 1570
Email: dmcgookeys@juno.com

ISBN 0-9719271-1-1
Library of Congress Control Number: 2004094204

Printed in Korea

This book is dedicated with love and appreciation to

Doris Jean McGookey

and

Douglas Alan McGookey

Contents

Contents (cont.)

Digital mosaic of 31 Landsat images of Texas. Courtesy of John Everett and Earth Satellite Corporation. Website: www.earthsat.com

Geologic Wonders of West Texas
Chapter 1
Introduction

Geologists have long known the joy of stopping along highways or hiking the backcountry of West Texas, and studying the geology. Some examples: (1) stopping on Highway 71 across the Llano Uplift to study one/half billion year old sandstones or 1.2 billion year old metamorphic rocks; (2) hiking to the South Rim of the Chisos Mountains and drinking in the scenery and geology observed from that ridge; (3) sampling the inside of a volcano in road cuts along US 90 west of Alpine; (4) walking the Skyline Drive in the Davis Mountains State Park and speculating on the Yellowstone-like terrain of hot springs and geysers that existed over the Davis Mountains 35 m.y. ago; and (5) seeing a great barrier reef from inside out on a hike to Pratt's cabin in McKittrick Canyon of the Guadalupe Mountains National Park. This book is an attempt to share the wonders of West Texas geology. It is not inclusive. West Texas is a huge area and there are geologic features that are not covered.

A geologist is basically a historian who reconstructs the history and paleogeography by studying the succession of rocks that crops out at the surface or is penetrated in all kinds of wells. Geologists use other scientific disciplines in this study including chemistry, physics, biology, and mathematics. Geologists have natural laws, like the **Law of Superposition**, that are unique to this science. In this book tables and listings of sequences of events or rock formations will reflect the Law of Superposition and always be compiled with the oldest events, formations and rocks at the bottom and youngest on top.

The rocks of West Texas record events during the last 1.5 billion years (b.y.) of the history of the planet Earth, which was formed about 4.6 b.y. ago. The Geologic Column (inside front cover) shows the names assigned to successive age units. Figure 1 of the Introduction Chapter is a geologic column for West Texas. The geologic history of West Texas includes large gaps where there is no rock record. Surprisingly, in the following chapters we shall see that the rock record indicates West Texas was at or near the equator for hundreds of millions of years.

If you encounter words and terms that are not familiar, please check to see if they are described in the Glossary at the end of the book. For those new to geologic science I recommend that they acquire college freshman physical and historical geology textbooks from the county or local college library, used bookstores, or Friends of the Library sale. Any textbook published in the last 20 years will be beautifully illustrated. By leafing through these books and reading the figure captions, one will become familiar with many concepts of geology that will help in reading this book.

HISTORY OF WEST TEXAS

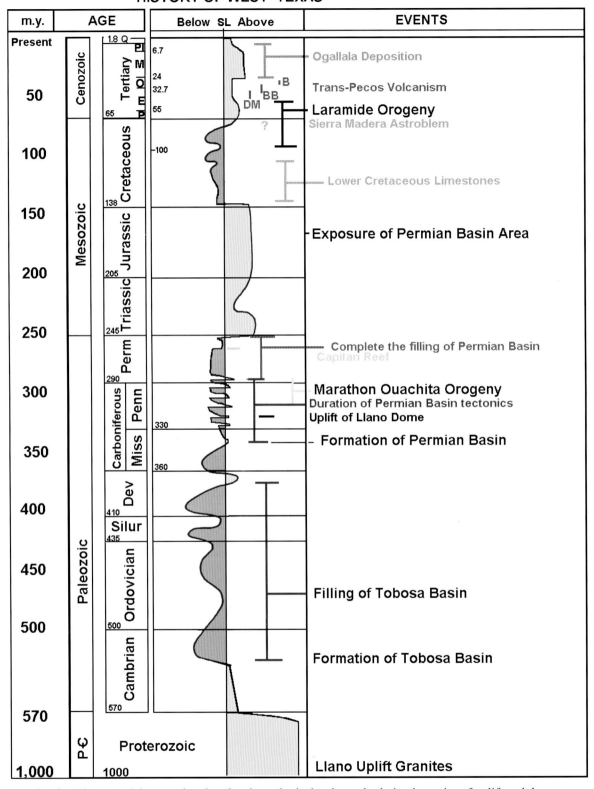

Introduction Figure 1. Diagram showing the chronological order and relative intensity of uplift and downwarp events in West Texas. Times when the West Texas area was partially or completely covered by marine water are colored blue. Times when this area was above sea level and receiving non-marine sediments are colored orange (after Hills, 1972). DM=Davis Mountains. BB=Big Bend. B=Bofecillos.

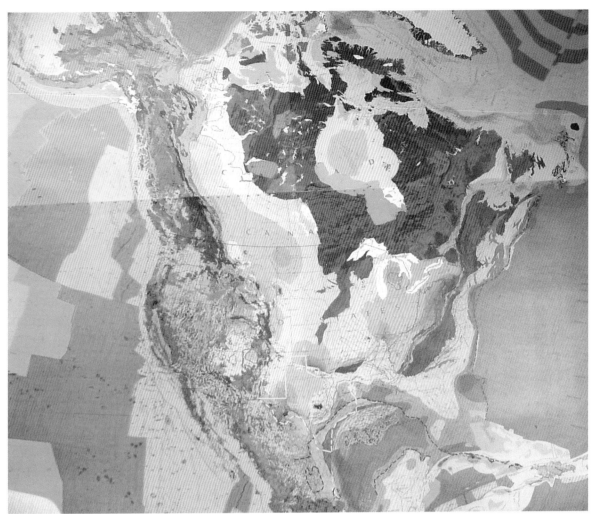

Introduction Figure 2. Tectonic Map of North America (Muehlberger, 1992).

The rock record shows that the area covered by Texas is and throughout geologic history has been on the edge of the North America Continent. Introduction Figure 2 shows mountain belts and the age of the rocks at the surface in these belts. It also is colored to show areas of the continent that have similar deposition or volcanic histories. For instance, East Texas has geology in common with other areas colored gray across the north side of the Gulf of Mexico Basin. Most of West Texas is colored pink and is seen as a southwest spur to the pink areas (a series of basins of deposition) that extend westward from New York State in a gigantic arc to the Arctic Ocean. Inside this arc are outcrops of Precambrian rocks that center around Hudson Bay. The older rocks are the Precambrian core area of the continent (please see Llano Uplift Figure 1 for a picture of the growth of the continent during Precambrian time). The pink shaded areas indicate that the rocks in those basins are Paleozoic in age. The darker pinks indicate the deeper parts of each basin. Far West Texas with its many colors is a southeast continuation of the complex geology of the Rocky Mountain area.

The state of Texas is divided geologically into an older part and younger part by a buried mountain range, the Ouachita Trend. This trend is buried by several thousand feet of younger rocks (mainly Cretaceous rocks) over most of its extent, but is exposed at the surface in two areas, the Marathon Uplift of West Texas and the Ouachita Mountains of Oklahoma and Arkansas. Study of the Texas Geologic or Tectonic Maps (Introduction Figures 3 and 4) reveals a prominent change of rock type and structural character over the buried mountain trend that can be traced east from the Marathon Uplift to San Antonio. The trend then curves to north-northeast (approximately under Highway I-35) through Austin and Dallas (please see the Ouachita Trend posted on Introduction Figure 6).

The region of Texas east of this trend is part of the Gulf of Mexico Basin. This basin was formed early in Mesozoic time and has a history of progressive filling from Jurassic time to the Present. Cross sections from Dallas to the Yucatan peninsula show the Gulf of Mexico Basin has been filled primarily from the north by sediments carried by river systems of the North American continent. The Sigsbee Deep of the Gulf of Mexico, with water depths of over 13,000 feet, is deepest part of the unfilled part of the basin. The process of filling this basin is about two-thirds complete. Compare the Gulf of Mexico basin, in which the filling is still in progress, with the Permian Basin, which formed and was completely filled during the Paleozoic Era.

Sixty percent of Texas is west of the Ouachita Trend. West Texas is an entirely separate terrain of uplifts and basins that were developed and filled during the Paleozoic Era. Superimposed on parts of this terrain are large areas covered by: (1) Cretaceous limestones, (2) the products of Tertiary volcanism, (3) Late Tertiary continental rift systems, and (4) the remnants of a very large Late Tertiary alluvial fan deposit (Ogallala Formation).

Geologic Map of Texas

The geologic map (Introduction Figure 3) is one of several inexpensive page-size maps available from the Texas Bureau of Economic Geology in Austin. The Ouachita Trend underlies the green belt that runs through Austin and Dallas. This belt of outcrops includes the Cretaceous Austin Chalk. East of the Ouachita Trend the Geologic of Texas map shows a series of subparallel brown to yellow belts that represent the outcrop areas of Tertiary and Recent sediments. These belts become successively younger towards the Gulf of Mexico. Most of the sediments are soft (easily eroded) sandstones and shales of stream and near-shore sites of deposition. Included in the Eocene belt are coals that were deposited in swamps. Each successive rock sequence in this part of the state dips very gently towards the Gulf of Mexico. For a description of the history of formation and filling of this part of the Gulf of Mexico Basin please refer to *"Gulf Coast Cenozoic Sediments and Structure"* (McGookey, 1975, Transactions of the Gulf Coast Association of Geological Societies).

West of the Ouachita Trend the geologic map shows scattered blotches of blues, grays, greens, reds, and other colors representing rocks of Precambrian to Recent age. The explanation of various distributions of rock types and ages over much of the western area will be the focus of this book.

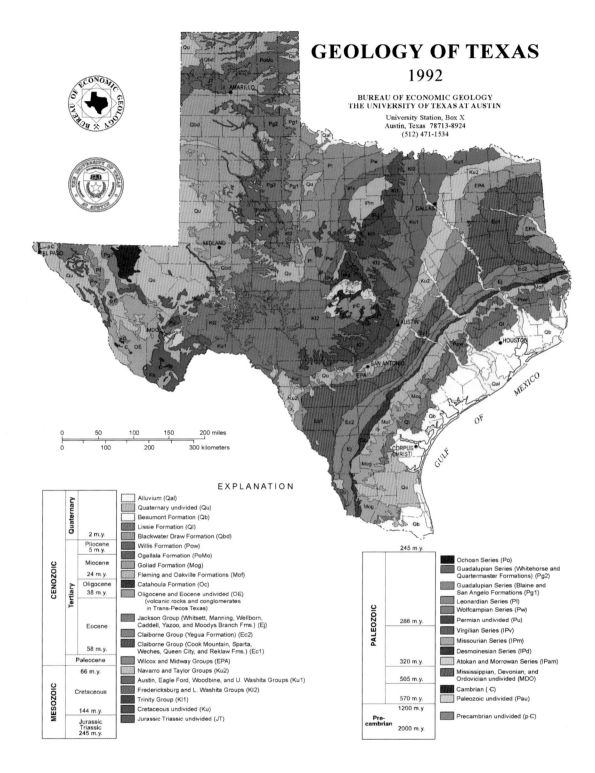

GEOLOGY OF TEXAS
1992

BUREAU OF ECONOMIC GEOLOGY
THE UNIVERSITY OF TEXAS AT AUSTIN

University Station, Box X
Austin, Texas 78713-8924
(512) 471-1534

EXPLANATION

CENOZOIC	Quaternary	2 m.y.	Alluvium (Qal)
			Quaternary undivided (Qu)
			Beaumont Formation (Qb)
			Lissie Formation (Ql)
			Blackwater Draw Formation (Qbd)
	Tertiary	Pliocene 5 m.y.	Willis Formation (Pow)
			Ogallala Formation (PoMo)
		Miocene 24 m.y.	Goliad Formation (Mog)
			Fleming and Oakville Formations (Mof)
		Oligocene 38 m.y.	Catahoula Formation (Oc)
			Oligocene and Eocene undivided (OE) (volcanic rocks and conglomerates in Trans-Pecos Texas)
		Eocene	Jackson Group (Whitsett, Manning, Wellborn, Caddell, Yazoo, and Moodys Branch Fms.) (Ej)
		58 m.y.	Claiborne Group (Yegua Formation) (Ec2)
			Claiborne Group (Cook Mountain, Sparta, Weches, Queen City, and Reklaw Fms.) (Ec1)
		Paleocene 66 m.y.	Wilcox and Midway Groups (EPA)
MESOZOIC	Cretaceous		Navarro and Taylor Groups (Ku2)
			Austin, Eagle Ford, Woodbine, and U. Washita Groups (Ku1)
			Fredericksburg and L. Washita Groups (Kl2)
		144 m.y.	Trinity Group (Kl1)
			Cretaceous undivided (Ku)
	Jurassic Triassic 245 m.y.		Jurassic Triassic undivided (JT)

PALEOZOIC	245 m.y.		Ochoan Series (Po)
			Guadalupian Series (Whitehorse and Quartermaster Formations) (Pg2)
			Guadalupian Series (Blaine and San Angelo Formations) (Pg1)
			Leonardian Series (Pl)
	286 m.y.		Wolfcampian Series (Pw)
			Permian undivided (Pu)
			Virgilian Series (IPv)
			Missourian Series (IPm)
	320 m.y.		Desmoinesian Series (IPd)
			Atokan and Morrowan Series (IPam)
	505 m.y.		Mississippian, Devonian, and Ordovician undivided (MDO)
	570 m.y.		Cambrian (C)
	1200 m.y		Paleozoic undivided (Pau)
Pre-cambrian	2000 m.y.		Precambrian undivided (pC)

0   50   100   150   200 miles
0   100   200   300 kilometers

Introduction Figure 3. Geologic Map of Texas (Bureau of Economic Geology). The colors used for each geologic time unit on this map are according to the standard colors used on all geologic maps and cross sections. For example, blue colors are Late Paleozoic; green are Cretaceous and earth tones are Cenozoic. These same colors will be used throughout this book. There may be exceptions where certain colors are selected to make figures easier to read.

Tectonic Map of Texas

On the Tectonic Map the eastern edge of the Balcones Fault Zone is over the approximate east edge of the buried mountains of the Ouachita Trend. The western edge (likewise buried) is identified as the Ouachita Tectonic Front. **Chapter 2 discusses the origin of the Ouachita Trend by a Late Paleozoic collision of continental plates** in a fashion similar to the collision of the Europe and African continental plates that formed the Alps of Europe. The trend is at the surface in the **Ouachita Mountains** of west-central Arkansas and southeastern Oklahoma, and again in the **Marathon Uplift** of southwest Texas.

Most of the features west of the Ouachita Trend are the result of uplifts and downwarps of the area during the Paleozoic Era (Chapters 3 and 4). These include all of the labeled basins, arches, platforms and uplifts. The formation of basins and uplifts occurred in two long intervals. The early history included the development and filling of the broad **Tabosa Basin** from Cambrian to Early Mississippian time. The later history, which included the formation and filling of the **Permian Basin**, from Late Mississippian to the end of Permian time, was more complex and contributed several major geologic wonders of West Texas.

During early and middle Mesozoic time, West Texas was above sea level and subject to erosion. Early in Cretaceous time, all of Texas was below sea level and covered by marine waters. Texas was part of a north-south seaway that formed across west-central North America from the Gulf of Mexico to the Arctic Ocean. The Texas part of the seaway was the site of warm, sub-tropical seas. Thick sequences of limestone were deposited during the Early Cretaceous, followed by thick sections of marine shale, and later non-marine sediments during the Late Cretaceous.

The Tertiary history of West Texas is confined primarily to the Trans-Pecos region (between the Pecos and Rio Grande Rivers). In that area there was a succession of: (1) early Tertiary Laramide tectonic activity; (2) Eocene and Oligocene igneous events that included intrusive and volcanic features; and (3) the southeast continuation of continental rifting during the Miocene to recent times. The Laramide events are the southern continuation of the structural activity that formed the Rocky Mountains. In response to the uplift that caused the Miocene and Pliocene rifts, erosion in the mountain areas fed an apron of sediment (the well-known Ogallala Formation) that was deposited east of the Rocky Mountains from West Texas to South Dakota. Erosion has reduced the apron to what we now call the High Plains, which in Texas is the broad east-sloping Llano Estacado plateau (discussed in Chapter 6).

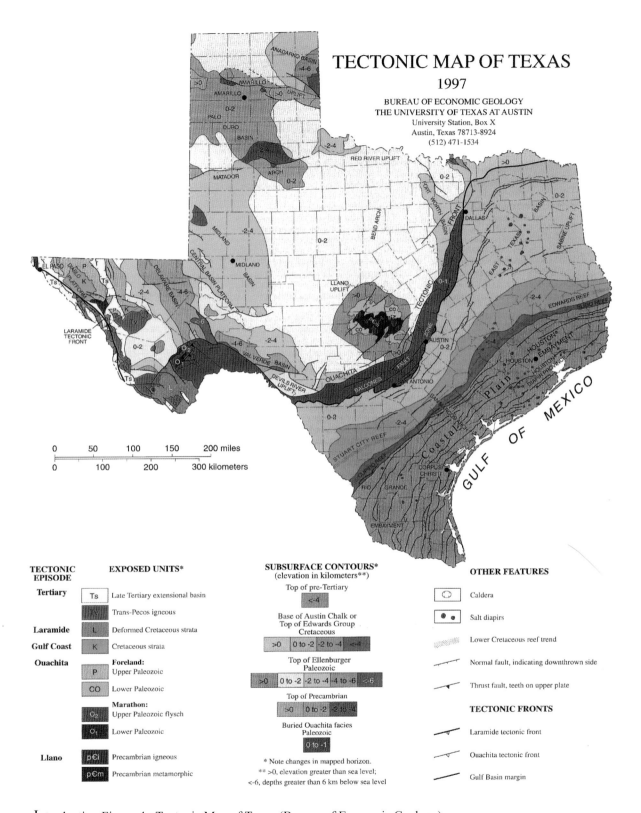

Introduction Figure 4. Tectonic Map of Texas (Bureau of Economic Geology).

Physiographic Map of Texas

The Ouachita Trend in the subsurface underlies the Balcones Escarpment (a topographic break along east edge of Edwards Plateau and Hill country). West of Interstate 35, limestone quarries are prominent in the Lower Cretaceous limestones exposed just east of the escarpment. Over the buried mountains the Lower Cretaceous limestones have been tilted to the east and disappear into the subsurface.

Southeast and east of Interstate 35 there are broad plains and prairies developed on soft Late Cretaceous and Tertiary sediments. There are several low relief escarpments across East Texas caused by the outcrops of prominent sandstones. Thick pine forests have developed on the sandstone hills.

West from Ouachita Trend there are two large plateaus, the Southern High Plains (Llano Estacado) and the Edwards Plateau. Northeast of the plateaus the topography is dominated by the southeast and east drainage systems of the Colorado, Brazos, Red and Canadian Rivers. Southwest from the plateaus, the Trans-Pecos Area is drained by the Rio Grande and Pecos Rivers. It is dry, arid and, fortunately, the geology is easily observed because of thin vegetative cover. The geologic features contribute a wild and dramatic landscape to the region and have spawned a number of national and state parks. .

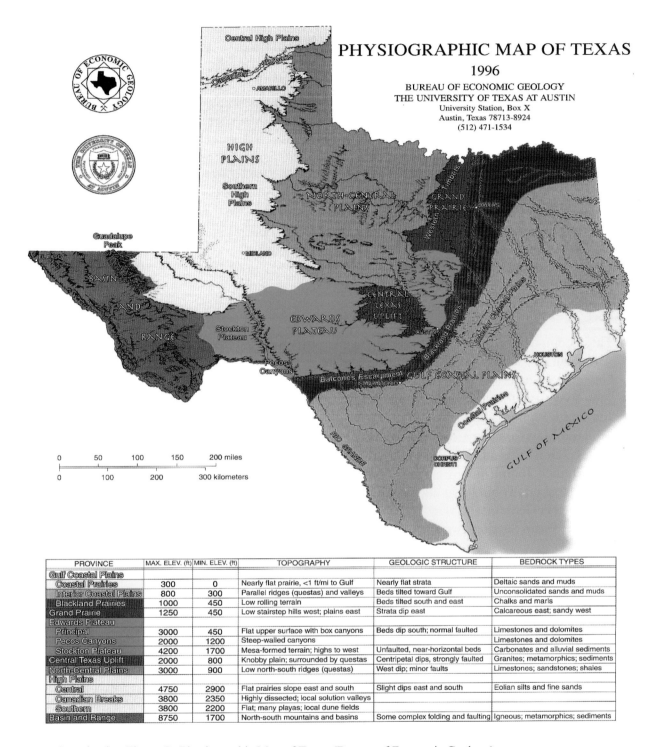

PHYSIOGRAPHIC MAP OF TEXAS
1996
BUREAU OF ECONOMIC GEOLOGY
THE UNIVERSITY OF TEXAS AT AUSTIN
University Station, Box X
Austin, Texas 78713-8924
(512) 471-1534

PROVINCE	MAX. ELEV. (ft)	MIN. ELEV. (ft)	TOPOGRAPHY	GEOLOGIC STRUCTURE	BEDROCK TYPES
Gulf Coastal Plains					
Coastal Prairies	300	0	Nearly flat prairie, <1 ft/mi to Gulf	Nearly flat strata	Deltaic sands and muds
Interior Coastal Plains	800	300	Parallel ridges (questas) and valleys	Beds tilted toward Gulf	Unconsolidated sands and muds
Blackland Prairies	1000	450	Low rolling terrain	Beds tilted south and east	Chalks and marls
Grand Prairie	1250	450	Low stairstep hills west; plains east	Strata dip east	Calcareous east; sandy west
Edwards Plateau					
Principal	3000	450	Flat upper surface with box canyons	Beds dip south; normal faulted	Limestones and dolomites
Pecos Canyons	2000	1200	Steep-walled canyons		Limestones and dolomites
Stockton Plateau	4200	1700	Mesa-formed terrain; highs to west	Unfaulted, near-horizontal beds	Carbonates and alluvial sediments
Central Texas Uplift	2000	800	Knobby plain; surrounded by questas	Centripetal dips, strongly faulted	Granites; metamorphics; sediments
North-Central Plains	3000	900	Low north-south ridges (questas)	West dip; minor faults	Limestones; sandstones; shales
High Plains					
Central	4750	2900	Flat prairies slope east and south	Slight dips east and south	Eolian silts and fine sands
Canadian Breaks	3800	2350	Highly dissected; local solution valleys		
Southern	3800	2200	Flat; many playas; local dune fields		
Basin and Range	8750	1700	North-south mountains and basins	Some complex folding and faulting	Igneous; metamorphics; sediments

Introduction Figure 5. Physiographic Map of Texas (Bureau of Economic Geology).

Acknowledgements

This book is complied from the contributions and publications of many as reflected in the number of selected references and the individuals acknowledged below. We are forever in debt to pioneers like P.B. King, Ross Maxwell, P. T. Flawn and J. M Hills. I also acknowledge the geologic contributions by many to publications of geological societies and the Bureau of Economic Geology. Thankfully, there has been a systematic coverage of regions by students and faculty at Texas universities. The amount of data available in the Petroleum-Technical Department of the Midland County Library makes study of West Texas especially rewarding. Like all scientific reports, this book is a progress report reflecting my knowledge to date of the geology and work of others. New studies, advances in technology, and improvement of sampling techniques are continually providing more geologic information and revising or correcting older concepts.

A very big thanks goes to Patricia Dickerson and Dianna Milewicz for detailed review of parts of the manuscript. Douglas McGookey edited and prepared the manuscript for the printer.

These companies and organizations have generously allowed me to use copyrighted figures:
American Association of Petroleum Geologists
Geological Society of America
John Everett, Earth Satellite Corporation, website: www.earthsat.com
Jon Smith Photographer
Midland Map Company, Midland, Texas
John C. Dohrenwend, Southwest Satellite Imaging, dohrenwend@rkymtnhi.com
Ray Sterner, John Hopkins University Applied Physics Laboratory
T. W. Neubert, Tobin International Ltd., San Antonio, Texas
West Texas Geological Society
Permian Basin Section, Society of Economic Paleontologists and Mineralogists

The following have generously contributed to this compilation.
Bruce Blake   Doris McGookey
Sigrid Clifty   Katherine McGookey
Jerry Dunnam   Gerald Mendenhall
Shirley Dutton   George Moore
Bill Grauten   Don Parker
Richard Guenther   Jay Raney
Richard Guenther   Sue Tomlinson Reid
Chris Henry   Lonnie Yee
Joel Lardon   Mick Denney
Andy Weinzapfel

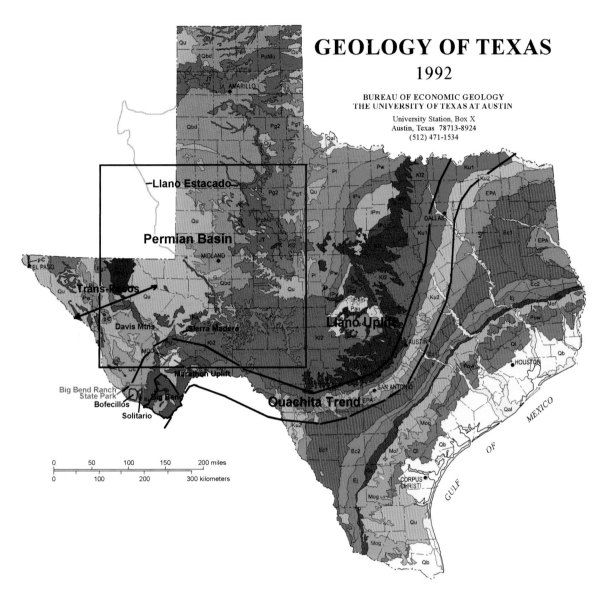

Introduction Figure 6. Geologic map with the location of geologic wonders featured in this book. Outlines of Llano Estacado, Big Bend and Big Bend Ranch State Park are approximate. Trans-Pecos region is the area in Texas between the Rio Grande and Pecos Rivers.

About the Author

Donald P. McGookey was born and raised in Sandusky, Ohio. He spent two years in the US Navy as an Electronic Technician. He earned his Bachelor's degree from Bowling Green State University, a Masters from the University of Wyoming, and a Ph.D. in geology at The Ohio State University. Texaco Inc. employed him from 1952 to 1979. Don worked in various parts of the Rocky Mountains for 17 years, in New York (International Exploration), and as Chief Geologist in Houston, Texas. Don ended his career with Texaco as manager of exploration in Midland, Texas. Since 1979, he has been an independent geologist working primarily in the Permian Basin of West Texas and southeast New Mexico.

Don's interest in West Texas began in 1971 during visits to Midland as Chief Geologist. During the 70's he participated in many geological society and company field trips to all parts of West Texas. In 1978, he was transferred to Midland and has lived there since. Fortunately, the whole family has enjoyed camping and hiking in West Texas, especially in the Big Bend region.

The research for this book has updated and expanded Don's knowledge of West Texas and improved his understanding of the Geologic Wonders that have resulted in great scenery and fascinating science. Hopefully, it has also resulted in a book that will help others enjoy these geologic wonders.

Chapter 2
The Ouachita Trend

In the Introduction Chapter the Ouachita Trend is described as a fundamental feature that physically divides Texas into two regions. Ouachita Figure 1 records a 1,300-mile long trend that snakes across four states. Throughout the length of the trend the Paleozoic age and types of rock involved remain very consistent. The rocks were deposited in deep submarine troughs along the edge of the North American continent. Starting in mid-Mississippian time, the sediments in the troughs were squeezed upward and thrust towards the continent. The thrusting stopped suddenly in early Permian time. That is the local part of the story. Please bear with me as I try to place these events in a plate tectonic context.

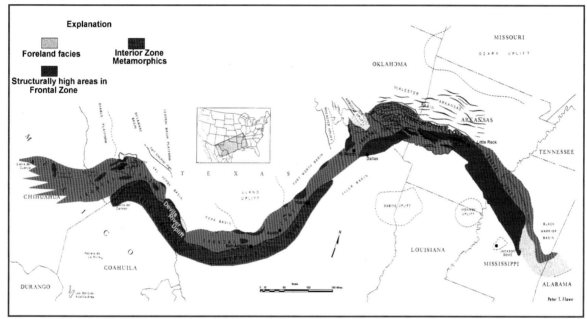

Ouachita Figure 1. The Ouachita Trend across southern United States (from Flawn et al, 1961).

The current concepts of plate tectonics conclude that all continents and ocean basins are underlain by convection systems in the mantle. The continent and ocean plates ride on the top of these systems like riding on a conveyor belt, and all plates are continually moving in one direction or another. Mountain ranges develop from: (1) collisions of continent-continent; (2) collisions of continents with small island continents (microcontinents) and (3) from the overriding of one plate over another plate (subduction). Continents increase in size (accretion) by the welding (addition) of island arcs (for example, Japan) or by the addition of island continents (for example the addition of India to Asia). **Currently, the North American continent is moving <u>southwest</u> at the rate of four centimeters per year.** This is at about the same rate that your thumbnail grows. **Throughout the Paleozoic Era (545 to 245 m.y. ago), the North American continent was moving <u>east</u>.** During the early and middle periods of this era, the continent collided with and welded to continental masses that are now Europe and North Africa, forming a mountain trend that extended from Georgia to the northern tip of Norway.

This docking with the other continents caused the eastward movement of the northern part of the continent to stop. The southern part of the continent was not confined and continued to move east.

During Late Paleozoic time, south of Mississippi, Arkansas, and the west part of Texas, there appears to have been a Mediterranean-type sea with oceanic crust. In this sea there were island microcontinents. The islands of Sardinia or Corsica in the Mediterranean Sea, and larger features such as Madagascar, are examples of present-day microcontinents.

The largest microcontinent evident today is India. Sometimes referred to as a sub-continent, it is actually a large microcontinent that is moving north and colliding with the southern part of the Asian continent. This collision has cause the formation of the Himalayan Mountain system. The collision is still taking place and Mount Everest is rising in elevation at the rate of nearly one centimeter a year.

In the same manner, small microcontinents in the Paleozoic Gulf of Mexico, such as the Sabine, Jackson, and Yucatan microcontinents, collided with the southern part of the North American continent in Late Paleozoic time. (Part of South America may have been involved). These **continent-microcontinent collisions formed a 1,300-mile long sinuous mountain system that is called the Ouachita Trend**.

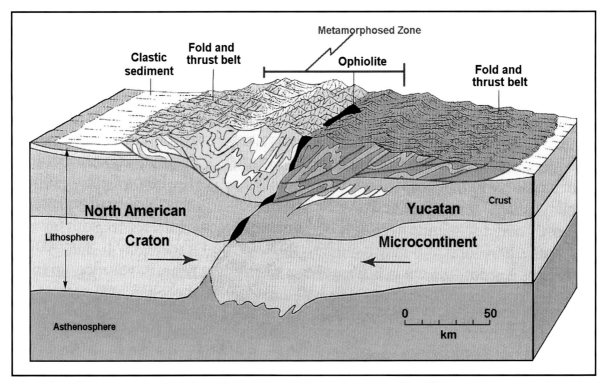

Ouachita Figure 2. Diagram of continent-microcontinent plate tectonic collision. The areas where the Ouachita Trend is at the surface in the Marathon Uplift and Ouachita Mountains are in the Fold and Thrust belt (Frontal Zone of Ouachita Figure 1) of the left side of the figure.

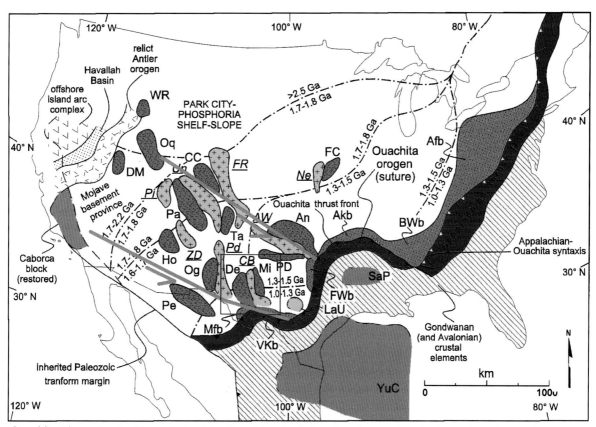

Ouachita Figure 3. Position of Ouachita Trend (red) relative to microcontinents (brown) to the south and east and the family of basins (blue) and uplifts (green) formed across the southwest part of the continent. **The Permian Basin is indicated by the square outline.** The latitudes are present day, not that of Late Pennsylvanian time when the Equator ran from central Arizona to southern Maine. Afb, Appalachian, AN, Anadarko, Ark, Arkoma, AW, Amarillo-Wichita, BWb, Black Warrior, CC, Central Colorado trough, CB Central Basin platform, De Delaware Basin, DM, Dry Mountain, FC, Forest City, FR, Front Range, FWb, Fort Worth, Ho, Holbrook, LaU, Llano Uplift, Mfb, Marfa, Mi, Midland Basin, Ne, Nemaha Ridge, Og, Orogrande Basin, Oq, Oquirrh, Pa, Paradox, PD, Palo Duro, Pd, Pedernal, Pe, Pedregrosa, Pi, Piute, SaP, Sabine and Jackson microcontinents, Ta, Taos trough, Un, Uncompahgre, VKb, Val Verde-Kerr, WR, Wood River, YuC, Yucatan microcontinent, ZD, Zuni-Defiance (after Dickinson and Lawton, 2003, p. 610).

Most of the Ouachita Trend is buried 3,000 to 6,000 feet below the surface at places like San Antonio, Austin, Waco, and Dallas. The complex faulting and folds of this belt are exposed at the surface in the **Ouachita Mountains of southeast Oklahoma and west-central Arkansas** and in the **Marathon area of southwest Texas**. There are other small exposures south and west of the Big Bend area of Texas. Across central Texas, the belt has been penetrated by numerous wells that were drilled for oil and gas. Flawn, et al, 1961 mapped this sinuous mountain system as including a highly deformed, but not metamorphosed, **Frontal Zone** and an **Interior Zone** that has highly deformed, metamorphic rocks. Almost all the exposed parts of the mountain system are part of the Frontal Zone, which has a maximum width of about 80 miles. This zone is characterized by shallow, low angle overthrust faulting of Paleozoic rocks towards the north or northwest.

The sedimentary rocks that are deformed along the Ouachita Trend were originally deposited in **deep-water troughs** that formed between the North American plate and the microcontinent plates. Because of the continent-microcontinent collision the contents of the troughs were squeezed upward and outward in Late Mississippian to Early Permian time.

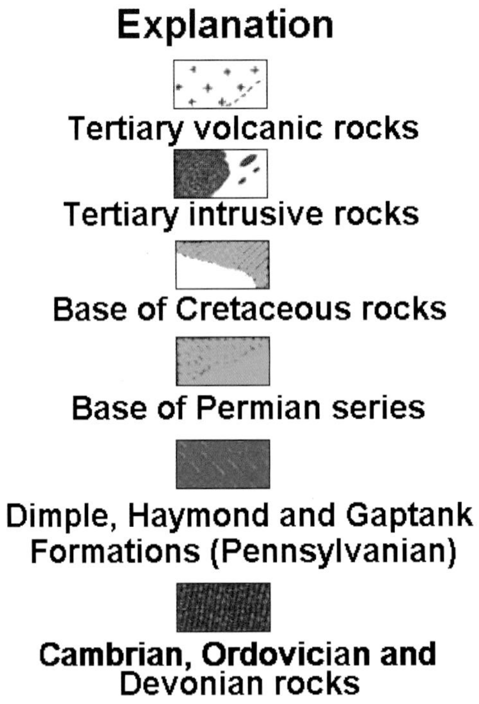

Explanation

Tertiary volcanic rocks

Tertiary intrusive rocks

Base of Cretaceous rocks

Base of Permian series

Dimple, Haymond and Gaptank
Formations (Pennsylvanian)

Cambrian, Ordovician and
Devonian rocks

Explanation for Ouachita Figure 4.

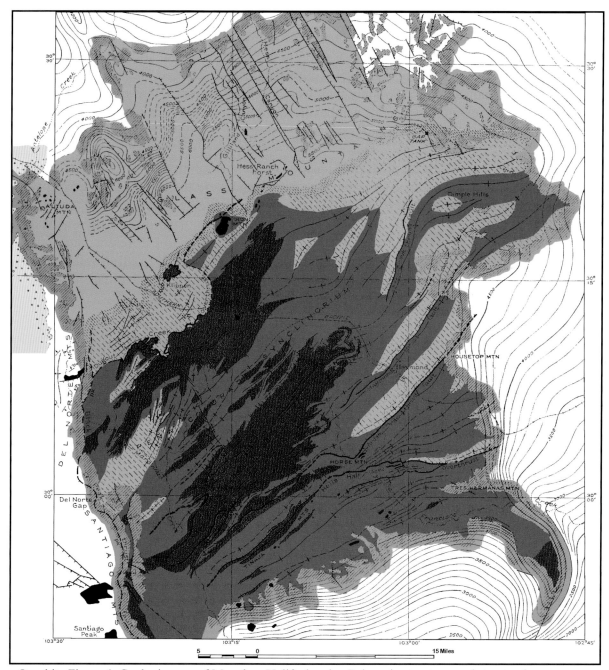

Ouachita Figure 4. Geologic map of Marathon Uplift showing Paleozoic structures and structural contours on the base of Cretaceous rocks.

In early Mesozoic time, the North American continent (with the Sabine and Jackson microcontinents now included by accretion) reversed direction of movement. The Yucatan plate appears to have rotated southward with the rest of Central America (and possibly part of South America) resulting in the opening of the present day Gulf of Mexico Basin. Study of the geologic history of Florida shows that area is a microcontinent plate left behind as the African and South American plates moved away from the North American Plate. Cuba is on another microcontinent plate.

The exposed rocks of the Ouachita Trend include limestones, sandstones, shales and novaculites. The sediments range from Cambrian to Late Pennsylvanian in age. There are no exposed rocks of Precambrian age. (Novaculites are bedded, recrystallized silica sediments of unknown origin. Possibly they were originally composed of the siliceous tests of microscopic plankton, or siliceous needles from sponges, or they may have resulted from a replacement of a carbonate section by silica).

Ouachita Figure 3 shows the approximate location of the microcontinents. The many uplifts and basins that developed inland from the Ouachita Trend were the result of the twist given to the continent by the continued eastward movement of the southern part of the North American continent. The orange wrench faults are added to diagrammatically show the relative rotation of separate sections of the continent that moved at different rates. The compression between the wrench faults caused the uplifts and basins **to all develop at the same time**. The Permian Basin, the subject of Chapter 4 in this book, is outlined with a red square.

Marathon Uplift

Terminology for the Marathon area may be confusing. The sediments of this area were folded and uplifted **(Marathon Uplift)** along overthrust faults to form the low relief **Marathon Mountains.** The uplifted area was above sea level when reefs that are now the **Glass Mountains,** (early to late Permian age) were deposited on the flanks of the Marathon Mountains. However, the Marathon Mountains rocks are primarily easily eroded soft shales so that today the former topographically high area has been reduced to a basin (**Marathon Basin**) and the flanking reefs, being made up of erosion-resistant limestones, are now the Glass Mountains that fringe the Marathon Basin on the northwest. To add to the confusion, there has been another uplift of the Marathon area since Cretaceous time so that at present a structure map on the base of the Cretaceous sediments shows a **domal uplift** (Ouachita Figure 4).

Ouachita Figure 5 (facing page). Satellite photo of Marathon area. Bars indicate width of anticlinoria. Reproduced courtesy of Tobin International Ltd. The Caballos Novaculite crops out as the light-colored stripe in the ridges of each anticlinorium.

The Paleozoic rocks exposed in the folds of the Marathon Basin have a thickness of 16,000 feet (King, 1937). Most of these sediments were deposited in a subsiding trough. The oldest rocks are Upper Cambrian sandstones and shales, whose base is not exposed. Overlying these rocks are 2,000 feet of Ordovician rocks that are composed of shaly limestone and shale with some beds of chert. The Ordovician is overlain by the Caballos novaculite, believed to be of Devonian age, which reaches 600 feet in thickness. This hard white siliceous rock is the chief ridge maker in the Marathon Basin.

Ouachita Figure 6. Caballos Novaculite in ridge next to Pina Springs, 5 miles south of Marathon, Texas.

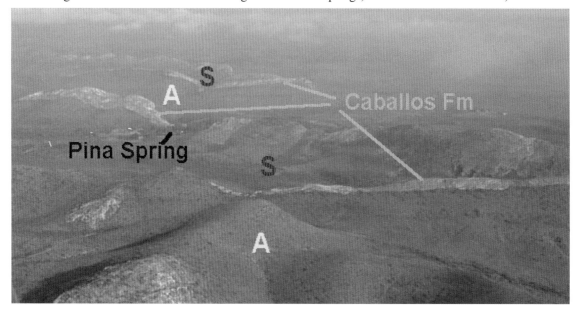

Ouachita Figure 7. Aerial view to southwest of folds of Marathon Anticlinorium near Pina Springs. A= Anticlines; S= Synclines. The Caballos Novaclite forms resistant ridges around each fold. Betty Hargus provided the airplane and Bob Elliott was the pilot.

The Caballos novaculite is overlain by a thick section of clastic rocks of mostly Pennsylvanian Age. This Late Paleozoic sequence is 12,000 feet thick in the southeastern part of the area, but much thinner in the northwest. Two of the lower formations are sequences of arkosic sandstones and shales that are separated by a widespread thin limestone formation. The two formations contain few fossils other than land plants. In the upper unit there is a remarkable layer of mudstone in which are embedded large blocks of older rocks. The blocks came from the southeast and are believed to have been derived from the erosion of advancing thrust sheets. They mark the first strong uplift in the region. They were probably transported to their present positions by turbidite flows. The uppermost Pennsylvanian formation consists of conglomerate and sandstone derived from the erosion of rising folds and contains Upper Pennsylvanian marine fossils.

The strong deformation of the Paleozoic rocks of the Marathon Basin culminated during the deposition of the uppermost formation of Pennsylvanian age, the Gaptank Formation. The Permian rocks of the Glass Mountains rest with great angular unconformity on the older beds.

The structural features seen in the basin consist of close folds (in cross section the folded rocks look like Christmas ribbon candy), trending northeast and overturned to the northwest. The folds are broken by numerous thrust faults. The faulting culminated on the northwest in the nearly flat-lying Dugout Creek overthrust. The horizontal displacement on the Dugout Creek overthrust fault is more than six miles (Ouachita Figures 8 and 9).

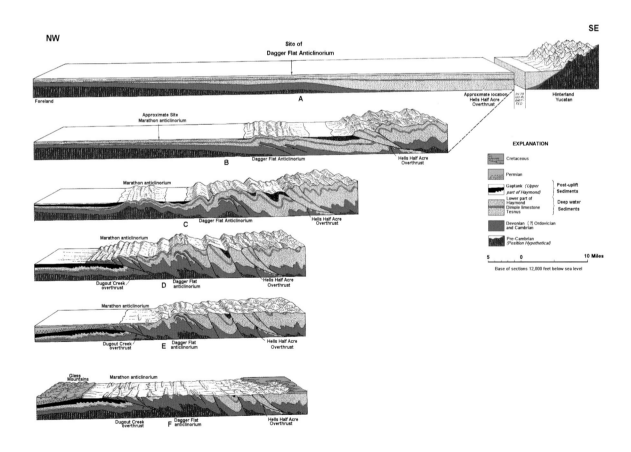

Ouachita Figure 8. Progressive development of the Marathon Uplift fold belts (from King, 1937).

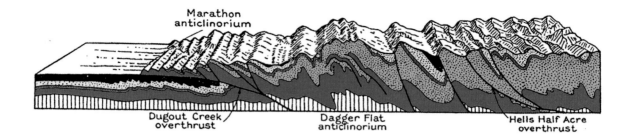

Ouachita Figure 9. Enlarged presentation of panel D of Ouachita Figure 8 (from King, 1937).

Ouachita Table 1. Paleozoic Section of Marathon Uplift and Glass Mountains

	Age	Formation
Post Uplift Formations	Permian	
	Ochoan	Tessey Limestone
	Guadalupian	Capitan Limestone (reef)
		Word Formation (reef)
	Leonardian	Cathedral Mountain Formation (reef)
		Skinner Ranch Formation and Hess Limestone (reef)
	Wolfcampian	Lennox Hill Formation
		Neal Ranch Formation
Contemporaneous with culminating uplift	Late Pennsylvanian	Gaptank Formation
Pre-uplift formations	Early Pennsylvanian	Hammond Formation (primarily shale)
		Dimple Limestone
	Late Mississippian to Early Pennsylvanian	Tesnus Formation (primarily shale)
	Devonian	Caballos Novaculite
		Maravillas Chert
	Ordovician	Woods Hollow Shale
		Fort Pena Formation
		Alstate Shale
	Cambro-Ordovician	Marathon Limestone
	Cambrian	Dagger Flat Sandstone

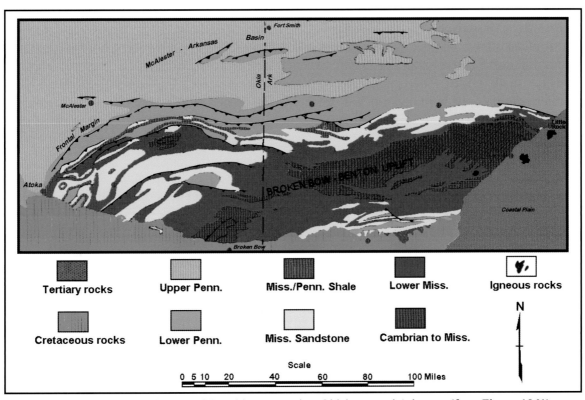

Ouachita Figure 10. Geologic Map of Ouachita Mountains, Oklahoma and Arkansas (from Flawn, 1961).

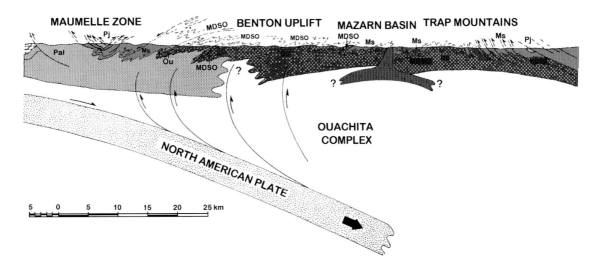

Ouachita Figure 11. Diagrammatic cross section of Ouachita Mountains (after Viele, 1979).

Across the exposed part of the Marathon Uplift three structural domains (western, eastern and southern) have mapped (Muehlberger and others, 1984). The western domain contains two anticlinoria and a synclinorium in which Lower Paleozoic rocks are exposed. Large folds in thick upper Paleozoic shale sequences characterize the eastern domain. The southern domain is bounded on the north by the Hell's Half Acre thrust fault and is composed of middle and upper Paleozoic sand and shale formations that are folded and imbricately thrust-faulted.

The Permian Reefs of the Glass Mountains are discussed in Chapter 4. The Cretaceous rocks that surround the Marathon Basin have a maximum thickness of about 1,200 feet and are mostly limestones. They were laid down on the eroded edges of the folded and tilted Paleozoic rocks, whose surface had been reduced to one of low relief during Triassic and Jurassic time. Within the region, small masses of igneous rock have intruded the Paleozoic and Cretaceous rocks.

Ouachita Trend in Central Texas

In the buried part of the Ouachita Trend, Marathon Uplift lithologic units and structures can only be traced for some tens of miles east of the outcrops. Over the rest of the buried Ouachita Trend, rocks similar to those exposed in the Ouachita Mountains, with the same kind of deformation, are recognizable in well cores and samples. An exception is present under southern Val Verde County, where there is a feature called the **Devils River Uplift** (Ouachita Figure 1). The rocks there have no outcrop equivalents. They include dark clastic rocks, metasedimentary rocks, metavolcanic rocks, and partly mylonized granitic rocks. They are believed to be metamorphic rocks of the Interior Zone that have been thrust north over those of the Frontal Zone.

Ouachita Mountains

The Ouachita Mountains of southeast Oklahoma and west central Arkansas consist of numerous nearly east-west trending ridges and several intermountain basins. The total area of the mountains is about 12,000 square miles.

The rocks of this part of the Ouachita Trend are a sedimentary sequence, called the **Ouachita facies**, which is very similar to the Marathon rocks. The Ouachita rocks include thin lower Paleozoic limestones, dark graptolitic and siliceous shales, cherts, sandstones, Arkansas Novaculite, and a relatively thick upper Paleozoic dominantly clastic sequence that includes thick turbidite deposits. All of the sediments appear to have been deposited in very deep water (over 3,000 feet deep). The important change in stratigraphic character took place in Early or Middle Mississippian time between the Arkansas novaculite and the overlying shale. The rocks are very similar to those of the Marathon Uplift, but lack the Ordovician and Pennsylvanian carbonate sections. In both areas clastic rocks thicken and are coarser southward. Ouachita Mountain rocks are strongly folded, broken by reverse faults, and thrust northward or northwestward along a series of low-angle faults. Incipient to low-grade metamorphism occurs in the rocks along the axis of the Broken Bow-Benton uplift, an anticlinorium that forms the central part of the range.

Chapter 3
Llano Uplift

The word "unique" comes to mind when looking at the features of the Llano Uplift. The uplift is a broad domal feature in central Texas that is one of the family of uplifts and basins formed across southwestern North American during Late Paleozoic time (please see discussions in Chapters 2 and 4). Erosion of this dome by the Colorado River and its tributaries has provided a unique opportunity to view Late Proterozoic rocks at the surface in the United States. There are small outcrops of Proterozoic rocks near El Paso and Van Horn, Texas, in the Arbuckle and Wichita Mountains of Oklahoma, and in the Ozark Mountains of Missouri, but they are all older than the Llano Uplift sequence. The next closest outcrop of Precambrian rocks of the same age as the Llano Uplift rocks is over a thousand miles northeast in Ontario and Quebec (LU Figure 1). There is one exception, the age of the granites of the Pikes Peak Batholith that centers near Colorado Springs are nearly the same as the Town Mountain Granite of the Llano Uplift.

This chapter will provide an introduction to the exposed Precambrian and Lower Paleozoic rocks along with detailed maps and discussion of some of the interesting outcrops. For the traveling public there is a road log along State Highway 71 from northwest to southeast across the entire uplift.

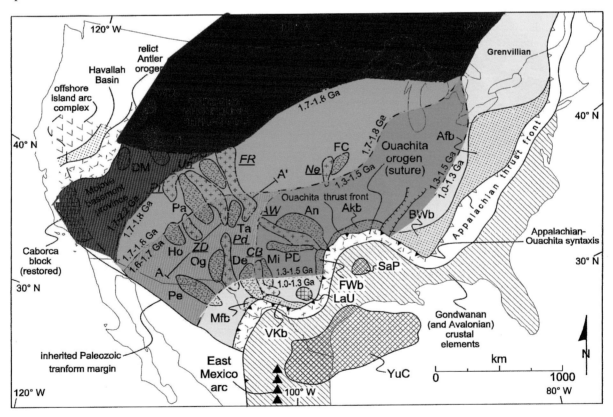

Llano Uplift (LU) Figure 1. This map shows the location of the Llano Uplift (LaU on map) relative to parts of the continent accreted during the Proterozoic. The age of each addition to the continent is posted within the colored belts. Ga=billion years. Llano Uplift area is part of the Grenvillian, the youngest of the Proterozoic additions. The red area is the Archean core area of the continent (from Dickinson and Lawton, 2003).

About every part of the Llano Uplift has been studied, mapped in detail, and reported in publications. The exposed Precambrian section covers over 2,000 square miles. About 60 percent of the outcrops are regionally metamorphosed gneisses and schists. The balance of the area has large exposures of a succession of approximately one billion year old granites that intrude the older rocks.

The Paleozoic section that overlies the Precambrian rocks includes a Late Cambrian section dominated by thick sandstones and an Early Ordovician section of carbonates. Late Ordovician, Silurian, and early Devonian rocks were deposited over the uplift area, but were deeply eroded and are now recorded only by pebbles deposited in sink holes in the karst topography developed on the top of the Early Ordovician carbonates. The early Pennsylvanian uplift of the dome was accompanied by the development of numerous radial faults. The radial faults do not displace rocks younger than the Early Pennsylvanian rocks. A very easily identified angular unconformity between Early and Middle Pennsylvanian rocks can be viewed in the exposed rocks of the northeast, north, and west flanks of the uplift. Cretaceous rocks cover the south side.

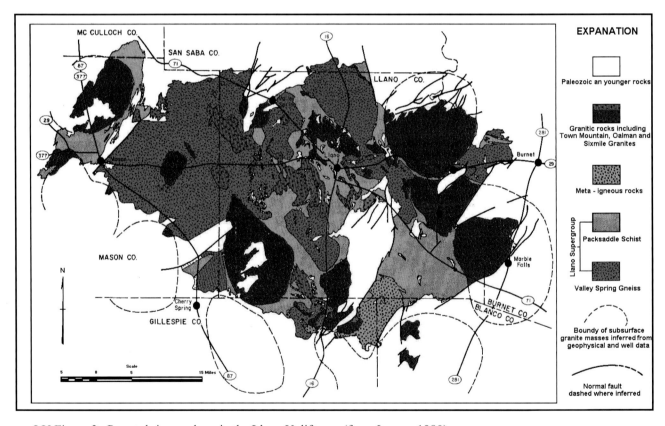

LU Figure 2. Precambrian geology in the Llano Uplift area (from Jensen, 1980)

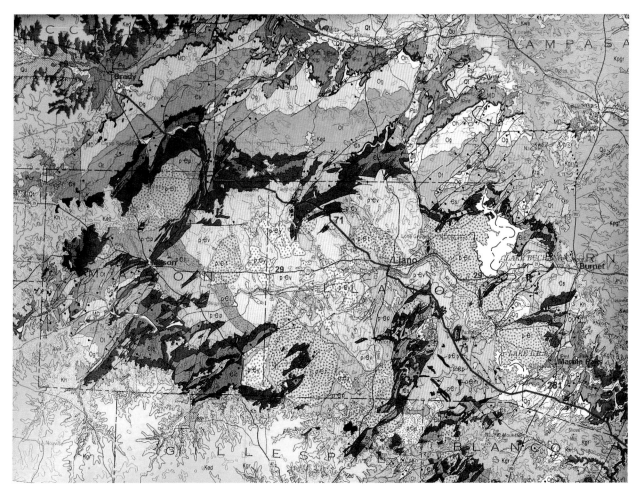

LU Figure 3. Geologic Map of Llano Uplift area. Red line is Texas Highway 71. Please see Geologic Column for symbols (from American Assoc. Petroleum Geologist's Geologic Road Map of Texas).

Geologic Column

Lower Cretaceous Rocks	Ordovician and Cambrian
(Not differentiated here)	Tanyard Formation *Ot*
Paleozoic Rocks Undifferentiated *Pal*	Wilburns Formation (part)(*Cw*)
Pennsylvanian	Cambrian
Lower Pennsylvanian	Upper and Middle Cambrian
Strawn Group *lPpbr*	Wilberns Formation (part)
Smithwick Shale *lPsw*	Riley Formation *Cr*
Marble Falls Limestone *lPmf*	Lion Mountain Sandstone *Crc*
Unnamed phosphorite	Cap Mountain Limestone *Crc*
Mississippian *MD*	Hickory Sandstone *Crh*
Barnett Formation	
Chappel Limestone	**Precambrian**
Mississippian and Devonian *MD*	**Igneous Rocks** (970-1070 m.y.)
Houy Formation	Llanite (blue quartz porphyry dikes) *pCl*
Doublehorn Shale	Sixmile Granite *pCy*
Ives Breccia	Oatman Creek Granite *pCtm*
Devonian	Town Mountain Granite *pCtm*
Bear Spring Formation	**Meta-Igneous Rocks**
Unnamed limestone	Metagabbro and metadiorite
Stribling Formation	Red Mountain Gneiss *pCrm,mg*
Pillar Bluff Formation	Big Branch Gneiss *pCbb*
Silurian	**Metasedimentary Rocks**
Starcke Limestone *Ss*	Packsaddle Schist *pCps*
Ordovician	Lost Creek Gneiss *pClc*
Upper Ordovician	Valley Spring Gneiss *pCvs* (1120 m.y.)
Burnam Limestone *Ob*	
Lower Ordovician	
Ellenburger Group	
Honeycut Formation *Oh*	
Gorman Formation *Og*	

Precambrian

The Precambrian eras cover geologic time from the formation of the earth to the time of appearance of the first fossils with hard parts (shells and exoskeletons). The current concept is that this period extended from 4.6 to 0.545 billion years (b.y.) ago. The Precambrian rocks of the Llano Uplift have been dated from 1.17 to 0.97 b.y., and thus fall in the later part of the Precambrian history. The exposed section includes regionally metamorphosed rocks that were intruded by igneous rocks, most of which were granites. The metamorphic rocks originally were a very thick section of sedimentary rocks with intervals of extrusive volcanic rocks and intrusive rocks near the top of the sequence. This section was buried deep enough and subjected to heat and pressure that caused a complete recrystalization of the original minerals in the sediments and igneous rocks to their metamorphic equivalents. The radioactive clock sets the date of recrystalization at around 1.17 b.y. The granitic igneous rocks were intruded from 1.07 to 0.97 b.y. There are a few llanite and mafic dikes that post-date the granite intrusions.

Metamorphic Rocks

The metamorphic rocks are collectively called the **LLANO SUPERGROUP**. They include (1) an **older Valley Spring Gneiss,** (2) the **Packsaddle Schist Group,** and (3**) igneous rocks** that were intruding into rocks of the Supergroup prior to metamorphism. The metamorphosed intrusive rocks are exposed primarily in the southeast part of the Llano Uplift. Barnes, et al, (1972, p. 22) estimate the original sediments of the gneiss and schist sequences to have been over 20,000 feet thick. This indicates deposition in a deep basin that was probably located at the edge of the continent at that time. All the rocks in the supergroup were regionally metamorphosed. There are areas around some of the granite intrusives that show local contact metamorphism.

VALLEY SPRINGS GNEISS is exposed over large areas of the Llano Uplift. It is primarily a thick sequence of pink, fine to medium-grained, quartz-feldspar gneiss. The original deposits included rhyolitic volcanic rocks, some more ordinary sediments including arkosic sandstone, siltstone and, locally, a little limestone (sometimes metamorphosed to graphite). These deposits are typical of those found in an island arc, like the present-day Japanese island arc. After severe metamorphism, the resulting rock is often hard to distinguish from granite. The rock is rich in feldspar and quartz and outcrops weather with the same exfoliation pattern. Across the Llano Uplift, the Valley Spring Gneiss is usually harder and more resistant to erosion than the granites. The contact between the Valley Spring Gneiss and Packsaddle Schist is conformable.

The **Lost Creek Gneiss** occurs as a recognizable unit only in the northwest part of the Llano Uplift. Lost Creek Gneiss is quartz-feldspar-hornblende-biotite gneiss. The original rocks are interpreted to have been a sequence of arkose, shale, and rhyolitic lavas. This gneiss has a sharp contact with the Valley Spring Gneiss and a sharp to gradational contact with the overlying Packsaddle Schist.

The original **PACKSADDLE SCHIST GROUP** sediments had great variety and were deposited in a rapidly sinking trough. The sediments included magnesium and iron-rich muds, limestone and dolomite, calcareous sulfide-rich muds, clean white clays and siltstones, arkosic sandstones, some volcanic rocks, and all mixtures of these. The water was shallow, and limestone reefs and near stagnant lagoons were present at times. Gradually, the water deepened and the influx of sands and shales increased while the carbonate deposition ceased. There were outpourings of basaltic lava and intrusions of gabbroic rocks as deformation began in the trough. The sequence has four divisions listed below from youngest to oldest:

Click Formation. This upper unit has 3,410 feet of light brown to pink leptite (a fine-grained metamorphosed rhyolite) and quartz-feldspar schist in the lower part overlain by 3,800 feet of hornblende schist.

Rough Ridge Formation. This is a very thick formation of gray leptite of extremely uniform lithology. Other lithologies in the section include white muscovite schist in the lower half and gray biotite schist near the middle. The formation is 5,370 feet thick.

Sandy Formation. This formation is leptite, hornblende schist, and tremolite (an iron-magnesium mineral) schist. The formation is 2,290 feet thick. The top is picked at the top of highest hornblende schist.

Honey Formation. The lowest unit of the Packsaddle schist contains hornblende schist and leptite at the base that is overlain by complex lithologies that include marble, graphite and various other schists. The Honey Formation is at least 8,290 feet thick. The top of the formation is picked at the top of the highest marble.

METAINTRUSIVE ROCKS

These rocks were originally intruded into the rocks of the Llano Super Group, especially in the southeast part of the uplift. They were metamorphosed at the same time as the rest of the group.

Big Branch Gneiss. This intrusive is a gray, fine to course-grained, quart-feldspar gneiss and is usually described as a metamorphosed quartz diorite. It intrudes both the Valley Springs Gneiss and the Packsaddle Schist in the southeast part of the uplift.

Coal Creek and Oxford Serpentinites. Serpentine is a metamorphosed ultramafic igneous rock. It is a magnesium-rich rock that has been prospected as a potential source of that element north of Willow City. It is younger than the Big Branch Gneiss. The outcrop pattern suggests that it may have been a large sill.

Red Mountain Gneiss. This gneiss occurs as numerous sills in the upper part of the Packsaddle Schist. The rock was originally a pink granite.

Unnamed amphibolite bodies. These are interpreted as gabbro dikes and sills with several stages of emplacement.

Unnamed hornblende-plagioclase rock body. This is a metamorphosed diorite that crops out in a hill 3,000 feet southeast of Click, Texas.

Unnamed soapstone bodies. Soapstone occurs in the southeast part of the uplift in association with the Coal Creek Serpentinite and some amphibolite bodies.

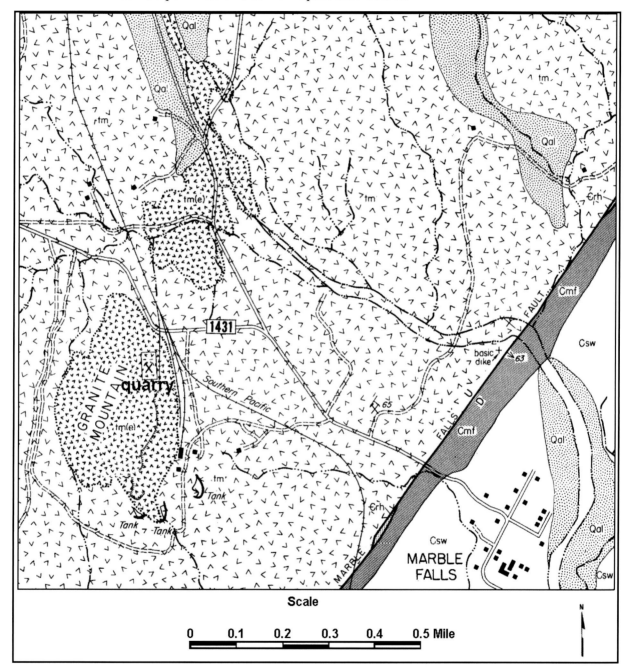

LU Figure 4. Geologic Map of Granite Mountain area west of Marble Falls (from Barnes, 1972, p.19). Please see LU Figure 17 for location. The high angle fault west of Marble Falls has a displacement of over 3,000 feet. The rounded dome of granite labeled Granite Mountain is also called Hog Mountain. The rock quarried is coarsely crystalline Town Mountain Granite that is relatively free of impurities. The granite takes a good polish, is of excellent grade and widely used as a building stone (State Capitol Building) and facing of buildings, floors, trim and counters in interiors, etc. Symbols are posted on LU Table 1, Llano Uplift Geologic Column. On this map tm= Town Mountain granite; tm (e)=larger exfoliated domes and bare rock surfaces.

IGNEOUS ROCKS

The igneous rocks are predominately **granites** that intrude the metamorphosed rocks of the Llano Supergroup. The intrusives have a variety of forms including laccoliths, stocks, sills and dikes. The very large semi-round granite outcrops look like bubbles on the top of a batholith. One gets the impression that deeper erosion of the Precambrian section would remove enough metamorphics to expose a very large batholith underlying the whole area.

Town Mountain Granite. This granite is the oldest, is widespread, and crops out over most of the uplift. It is pink, coarse-grained granite with large feldspar crystals. The contact of the Town Mountain Granite with country rock is usually sharp. Flow structure and xenoliths (inclusions) of metamorphic rock are common near the borders of the granite. There are some exposures where metamorphic rocks are intruded by numerous sills of the Town Mountain Granite.

The Town Mountain Granite is used widely in Texas as a building stone and riprap. The capital and other government buildings in Austin are built using Town Mountain Granite. If you are so inclined, you can walk a mile out into the Gulf of Mexico (and check the fishing) on the Bolivar Point breakwater that is made of large granite blocks.

LU Figure 5. Looking south into the granite quarry west of Marble Falls.

LU Figure 6. This outcrop of Town Mountain Granite in Enchanted Rock State Park is ideal for studying the rock while climbing.

LU Figure 7. Example of exfoliation weathering of Town Mountain Granite in Enchanted Rock State Park. This type of "onion layer" erosion is also present on the flanks of LU Figure 6.

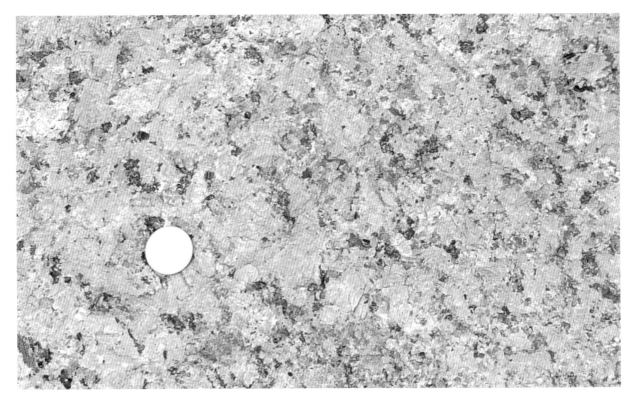

LU Figure 8. Close-up of Town Mountain Granite in outcrop two miles east of Katency in northern part of Mason County. Coin is a quarter.

Oatman Creek Granite. This granite is the second oldest intrusive body that occurs as dikes and sills in the Packsaddle Schist. It is gray to pink, medium-grained granite that appears to have the same composition and to be a later intrusion from the magma that was responsible for the Town Mountain Granite.

Sixmile Granite. This granite intrudes all older units. It is gray fine-grained granite that crops out as irregular masses and is also a later intrusion from magma body that fed the Town Mountain Granite. Some of the older buildings in Llano, Texas have corner columns of Six Mile Granite and walls of Hickory Sandstone.

Topaz. This mineral is the state gemstone of Texas. It is found in three areas north and northwest of Mason (Simpson, 1958). The sites are near Katemcy, Grit and Streeter, all in Mason County. The gemstones are found in gravels eroded from pegmatites (granite dikes with very large crystals) that intrude Town Mountain granite.

Dikes. Emplacement of the large granite bodies was followed by smaller intrusions of granite magma in the form of a few small dikes. The most famous are the distinctive **llanite dikes**. This rock consists of crystals of pale blue opalescent quartz and red microcline in a darker microcrystalline groundmass. Limited exposures of llanite dikes occur about 10 miles north of Llano, Texas, one of which is exposed in a State Highway 16 road cut.

LU Figure 9. Outcrop of llanite dike intruded into Valleys Springs Gneiss in Texas Highway 16 road cut 10 miles north of Llano.

Summary of Precambrian History

Probably as a result of collision of this part of the North American plate with another plate, the sediments of a trough near the edge of the continent were progressively affected by relatively high temperatures and pressures and regionally metamorphosed (recrystallized). There were intrusions of sills of mafic igneous rocks, quartz diorite, and the Red Mountain granite before regional metamorphism and deformation ceased.

Sometime after this metamorphism period, about one billion years ago, magmas were formed at depth and granite magmas rose and intruded the older rocks. Emplacement of the large granite bodies was followed by invasions of granite magma with smaller crystals and ultimately by the injection of a few small granite dikes.

The metamorphism and later granite magma formation appear to have resulted from the collision of the North American plate with other plates at about 1.0 b.y. as part of the formation of a super continent called Rodinia. An article on research work of Dr. Staci Loewy, of the University of

Texas (2003), includes a model that places the northern part of the Kalahari Plate of southern Africa on the other side of this part of the Grenvillian Trend.

During the next 400 million years uplift and erosion removed over a mile of rock and reduced a mountainous terrain to a subdued topography much like that today. This was the type of topography progressive buried as the Cambrian seas advanced across the region.

Sedimentary Rocks
Cambrian

Only Late Middle and Upper Cambrian time is recorded in two cycles of transgression and regression of marine waters over this part of the continent. Sediments deposited during the first cycle are assigned to the Riley Formation and the second cycle to the Wilberns Formation (Bell and Barnes, 1972).

Riley Formation

As the sea progressively flooded this area, quartz sandstones of the **Hickory Formation** were deposited. There was up to 800 feet of relief on the eroded Precambrian surface. The Hickory Sandstone contains 276 to 434 feet of sand that was deposited in shallow water. The sandstone ranges from fine to course grained and from clean quartz to arkosic. Locally, there is a mixture of iron ooids (BB-like grains) and quartz and feldspar grains (McBride,et al, 2002, p. 28) that was used as an iron ore during the 1800's. Regionally, the sand is exceptionally porous and permeable. It is soft, friable, and an excellent aquifer. There are two quarries in the northwest part of the Llano Uplift that provide bulk sand used in the hydraulic fracturing of oil wells.

Subsidence of the area during deposition of the Riley Formation was somewhat constant with deposition. As water deepened, 156 to 497 feet of limestones of the **Cap Mountain Formation** were deposited. The cycle ended with the deposition of 29 to 68 feet of **Lion Mountain Sandstone**. An erosional unconformity separates the Riley from the overlying Wilberns Formation.

Wilberns Formation

The second cycle is recorded in four members: **Welge Sandstone, Morgan Creek Limestone, Point Peak, and the San Saba Members**. Transgression of the sea is recorded in the 8 to 35 foot thick **Welge Sandstone**. This coarse to medium grained sandstone was deposited on a surface of low relief. It is overlain by a remarkably uniform 130 to 140 feet of fossiliferous, glauconitic **Morgan Creek Limestone**. Some strata are coquinites (a rock that is entirely made up of broken shells). There are also a few small stromatolitic bioherms (reefs). The **Point Peak** records a temporary influx of silt. The wave-agitated shallow-water depositional environment was conducive to the development of ripple marks, intraformational conglomerates (mud chips torn up and redistributed by storms, sometimes called flat-pebble conglomerates) and stromatolitic bioherms. Intraformational conglomerates are common in Cambrian sediments throughout western United States. Sometimes it is a very pretty rock with flat, light gray pebbles in a green shale matrix (LU Figure 11). The Point Peak ranges in thickness from 25 to 216 feet with a average thickness of 130 feet. The Point Peak contains silicified brachiopod shells is some areas. The **San Saba Member** is a 91-foot section of carbonates much like the Morgan Creek, but with intervals of intraformational conglomerates, abundant stromatolites, silicified brachiopod shells, and trilobites. In the extreme west there is a locally 23 to 69 foot sandstone. The contact with the overlying Ellenburger Group is conformable and laterally gradational.

LU Figure 10. This fault is exposed in a road cut at Mile Point 33.3 of Texas Highway 71Road Log. Both sides are Hickory Sandstones. Iron-rich sandstone on the right is displaced against normal Hickory Sandstone on the left.

LU Figure 11. Outcrop of Point Peak green shale and thin flat pebble limestone conglomerates along Farm to Market Road 2341 east of Lake Buchanan.

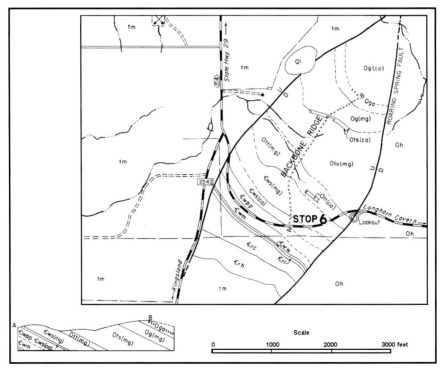

LU Figure 12. Geologic map of a fault wedge traversed by Inks Lake Park Road 4 two miles west of Longhorn Cavern (from Barnes, 1092, p.58). Please see LU Figure 17 for location. It is 0.7 miles from the picnic area at the lookout on top of the cliff (downthrown side of Roaring Spring Fault) to the junction with FM 2342. Several fossiliferous members of the Wilberns Formation can be studied in a walk down this road. All of the Ordovician members and formations identified on the map are of the Ellenburger Group.

Ordovician

The **Ellenburger Group** here is equivalent to the lower half of the Ellenburger (and equivalent formations) where a complete sequence is preserved, e.g. Ozark Uplift of Missouri and Arkansas. Over the Llano Uplift it is thickest in the southeast at 1,820 feet and thins to 830 feet in the northwest part. (Barnes and Cloud, 1972).

During Early Ordovician time warm marine waters covered the Llano. A current analog is the Bahama Banks east of southeast Florida. The widespread dolomitization of the original Ellenburger carbonate muds is interpreted to have occurred at the time of deposition.

Middle Ordovician sediments probably covered this area at one time. The only record is the presence of reworked conodont fossils of this age in basal Mississippian sediments in Blanco County. There is one small out crop of a pure fossiliferous limestone of Upper Ordovician age south of Marble Falls (Barnes and Cloud, 1972, Figure 13, page 35).

Silurian, Devonian and Mississippian

It was once believed that the post-Ellenburger, pre-Pennsylvanian sediments were missing from the Llano Region. Detailed mapping has corrected that idea as scattered clues to the former presence of sediments of these ages were found. The area was repeatedly covered by marine waters and layers of sediments deposited with each inundation. **The uplift exhibits a natural buoyancy** relative to surrounding areas so that each layer is stripped by erosion prior to the next inundation. The above paragraph recounted the evidence for Middle and Late Ordovician strata. Some of the other clues come from very small remnant outcrops while others have come from material dropped into collapse structures (karst topography) in the top of the Ellenburger carbonates. A trip through the Longhorn Caverns shows how solution cavities are filled. Many of the present Longhorn Cavern rooms and passageways were opened by excavating mud out of the tunnels.

In small outcrops and karst fillings the remnants of the following formations have been found:

Middle Silurian: brachiopods and trilobites in the Starcke Limestone.

Devonian: (1) a cave filling coquinite, the **Pillar Bluff Limestone**; (2) a thin basal sandy glauconitic dolomite and limestone that may be 1 to 11 feet thick; (3) the **Stribling Formation**; (4) a younger unnamed fossiliferous limestone in collapse structures: (5) another cherty granular limestone in collapse structures; and (6) at the top, the **Houy Formation**. The ill-defined Houy Formation may include units of Middle Devonian, Upper Devonian and Lower Mississippian age. Locally it has a black fissile, radioactive, spore-bearing shale up to 15 feet thick; a chert breccia, the **Ives Breccia,** that may be up to three feet thick and an upper phosphoritic unit that may be two feet thick.

Early Mississippian: crinoidal limestone and conglomerate outcrops of the **Chappel Formation**.

Late Mississippian: The next consistent sediment over the Llano Uplift is the **Barnett Shale,** a 40 to 50-foot brown shale. It is conformable with the Chappel Formation below and the Marble Falls above. Large ellipsoidal concretions are characteristic of the lower Barnett.

Pennsylvanian

The **Marble Falls Formation** is 200 to 250 feet of fossiliferous limestone. Often it includes a lower carbonate sequence, a middle shale and an upper carbonate. The fossils indicate that the Marble Falls is early Pennsylvanian (Morrowan) in age. Minor faulting and local unconformities in the Marble Falls section suggest that uplift is starting at this time.

The **Smithwick Shale** is a 60 to 400-foot, black, calcareous claystone and interbedded sandstone sequence that overlies the Marble Falls in Burnet County. This unit correlates with the Bend Formation farther north. Brachiopod, trilobite, goniatite and nautoloid fossils occur as impressions on shale partings. The deposits are described as muds deposited at the toe of an advancing delta.

The last major pulse of uplift occurred in late Atokan time (second subdivision of five in the Pennsylvanian) after the deposition of the Smithwick Shale and before the Strawn cyclic sequences. On all geologic maps there is a distinct angular unconformity. All faults that dissect the Llano Uplift are restricted to pre-Strawn rocks. The upper part of the uplift was stripped of all Lower Paleozoic rocks by the erosion caused by this uplift.

The Llano Uplift appears to have remained above sea level and was not the site of sediment deposition during the rest of the Paleozoic. The next episode of sedimentation over the Llano Uplift resulted when the area was inundated by the Early Cretaceous sea. Erosion since the end of the Cretaceous has removed post-Paleozoic sediments across the uplift area. There has been no tectonic activity after the Paleozoic era. The dip of Cretaceous strata away from the uplift is caused by a combination of the natural buoyancy of the uplift and subsidence in surrounding areas.

Road Log
Texas Highway 71 across the Llano Uplift
from just south of Brady to Llano and from Llano to Cretaceous
Rocks east of US Highway 281

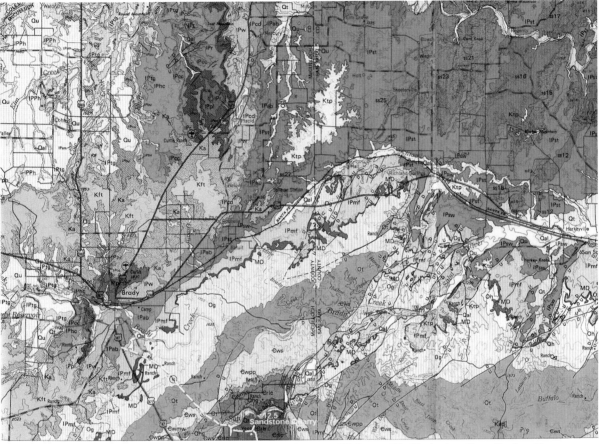

LU Figure 13. Geologic Map of northwest part of Texas Highway 71 (dashed yellow line). Please see Geologic Column in first part of this chapter for symbols. From Brownwood Sheet, Geologic Atlas of Texas.

<u>Mileage</u>

0.0   Junction US Highway 87 and Texas Highway 71. Go east on Texas Highway 71. Junction is at the angular unconformity contact between rocks of the Pennsylvanian Strawn Group and the Marble Falls Limestone, neither of which are exposed here. Please see the text of the Llano Uplift Chapter for a description of each of the rock units mentioned in this road log.

1.8   Thin chalky limestone about four feet thick. (Stribling Formation of Devonian age?) Massive carbonate rocks in road cuts below this limestone are the top of the Ordovician Ellenburger limestone and dolomite formation. The strata dip at about 5 degrees to the northwest.

2.2   Road north into Brady.

4.8   Crossing eroded Ellenburger outcrops. Note solution cavities filled with red soil. There are many caves in the Ellenburger around the north and east sides of the Llano Uplift.

7.4   Approximate base of Ellenburger and top of Cambrian Wilburns Formation.

7.7   Junction with county road to east. There is a northeast trending fault here that drops the Ellenburger rocks down in a graben (trough) between here and the east side of the San Saba River Bridge.

9.0   San Saba River Bridge. At east side cross fault into exposures of the Cap Mountain Limestone Member of the Cambrian Riley Formation.

9.4   Contact with the underlying Hickory Sandstone. This formation is an excellent aquifer around the west, north, and east sides of the uplift. The exposures usually formed low relief cliffs and are easy to identify. It is used extensively as a building and construction stone.

10.3   Picnic Area

11.9   Tiger Creek

12.1   Junction Farm to Market Road (FM) 1851 to left to Voca.

12.5   Entrance to Unimar of Texas Voca Plant. The Hickory Sandstone is quarried here. The Hickory is a clean quartz sand that is very soft and friable. Small explosive charges loosen the sand, which is then crushed, washed and put thought sieves to separate by size of grain. The sizes range from very fine to a course sand that has small round grains up to the size of a bb (2 mm). There is a very good market for the rounded course grains as a propping agent in hydraulic fracture treatment of tight sandstones in oil and gas wells. The fine sand fraction is used as a filter in water treatment plants.

13.4   Road to right goes past the quarry of Oglebay Norton Industrial Sands, a competitor with the same products from the Hickory Sandstone as the Unimar Plant.

14.1   Road cut exposes Packsaddle Schist.

14.3   Lost Creek

15.6   Road curves to south and crosses several faults in the next three miles. For the next 0.9 miles the road is on Lost Creek Gneiss, which underlies the Packsaddle Schist.

16.5   Hickory Sandstone in road cuts.

18.4   Ranch road to right. Hickory Sandstone in fault blocks here.

18.8   FM 366 to right to Fredonia. Texas Highway 71 curves to east and crosses a syncline (fault on east side).

18.9   Ellenburger outcrops in syncline.

19.2   Ellenburger dips east at 20 degrees.

20.1   Lost Creek Road. This is the approximate location of the fault on the east side of the syncline.

20.6   Curve to east on Hickory Sandstone.

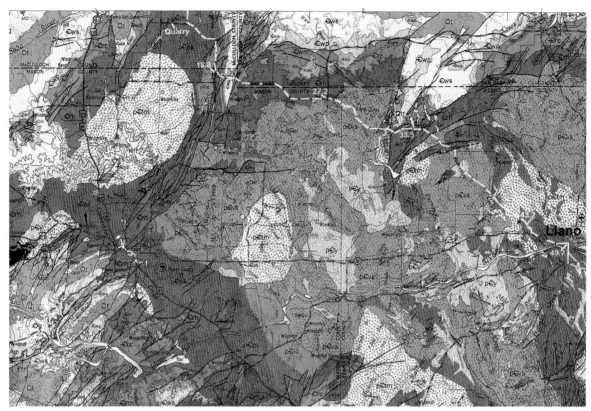

LU Figure 14. Geologic map of continuation of Texas Highway 71 northwest of Llano, Texas. Please note mileage marks on map. From Llano Sheet, Geologic Atlas of Texas.

25.4 Still on Hickory Sandstone.

26.4 Turn off to Pontotoc Cemetery. Valley Spring Gneiss outcrops here.

27.2 Pontotoc. Several buildings use local rocks, especially Hickory Sandstone, as facing.

28.3 Mason-Llano County Line.

29.2 Field Creek. Bedrock here is Valley Springs Gneiss.

31.2 Hickory Sandstone, entering a wide graben.

31.5 CR 405.

33.3 **Suggested stop.** Deep road cut through Hickory Sandstone. Please see Llano Uplift Figure 10 for a picture of the local iron-rich sand. Some of the outcrops are a deep blood red because of the high iron content. Close study reveals that the iron occurs as oolitic grains and also as a cement of the sandstone. There is a large hill to the south that is Town Mountain Granite capped by Hickory Sandstone, and a fault on the east side of the hill that displaces Hickory Sandstone against the Town Mountain Granite (Llano Uplift Figure 14). Farther east, on the other side of the graben, Town Mountain is again exposed. Thus the local circular bubble of granite is split by the graben.

33.6 The light colored rock in the hillside to the left (north) is the Cambrian Cap Mountain Limestone.

35.3   County Road to left. On Hickory Sandstone.

37.5   Valley Springs. At the curve east of the townsite there is another fault, beyond which are outcrops of the Valley Springs Gneiss (named for exposures in this area).

38.0   Valley Spring Gneiss exposures.

39.2   Here the Valley Springs Gneiss is intruded by the youngest of the granites, the Six Mile Granite. The Six Mile Granite is light fine-grained granite. The outcrop of this intrusive is wider than that shown on Llano Uplift Figure 14.

39.6   Six Mile Granite

43.2   Entrance to Old Quarry Ranch. Blocks in gate and wall are from a quarry (since 1895) on this ranch. This is a good place to view the Six Mile Granite and compare it with the much courser grained Town Mountain Granite. Six Mile Granite was used as a building stone in Llano.

44.7   Turn off to Wolf Mountain Boy Scout Ranch. The rocks exposed here are Town Mountain Granite.

46.0   Town Mountain Granite in Road Cut.

46.9   Junction with Texas Highway 29, turn left (east). Now on Packsaddle Schist, which is mostly covered by soil.

47.1   Small outcrop of Six Mile Granite intruding Packsaddle Schist.

49.7   Junction Texas Highways 71, 29 and 16. Llano is primarily underlain by Packsaddle Schist. There are local intrusive sills of Six Mile Granite.

Road Log of exposed rocks along Texas Highway 71 southeast from Llano to Spur 191

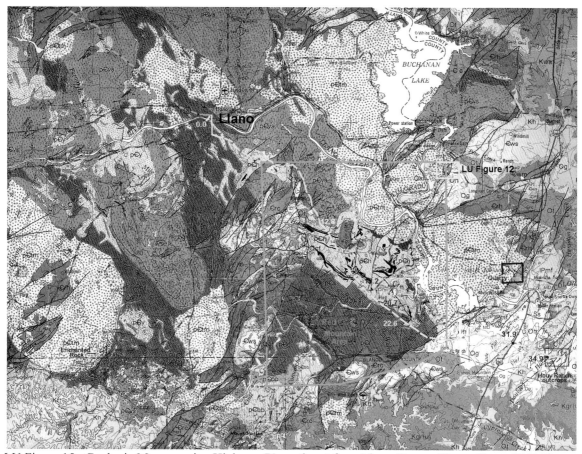

LU Figure 15. Geologic Map covering Highway 71 southeast from Llano, Texas. The outlines of LU Figures 4, 12, 16, and 18 are posted (Llano Sheet, Geologic Atlas of Texas).

<u>Mileage</u>

0.0   Junction Texas Highways 71, 16, and 29 on north side of Llano. Travel south on Highways 16/71.

0.3   Llano River Bridge. Packsaddle Schist is exposed in this area with local intrusive sills of Sixmile Granite. Some old buildings in Llano have corner columns of Sixmile Granite and walls of Hickory Sandstone blocks.

1.4   Junction Texas Highways 71 and 16, continue left (east) on Texas Highway 71.

2.7   Sixmile Granite in outcrops and road cuts.

4.1   Precambrian Honey Formation. This unit is at the base of the Packsaddle Schist Group. It includes hornblende, graphite and muscovite schists.

4.7   Bedded Honey schist.

5.7   Exotic animal farm on left (north).

5.9   Honey Formation.

6.6 Cross fault with Hickory Sandstone on downthrown (east) side.

7.1 Hickory Sandstone.

8.3 County road to right (south). Now on Honey Formation.

9.3 Driving southeast with Valley Springs Gneiss on the left and Hickory Sandstone on the right.

10.1 Valley Springs Gneiss.

12.2 Packsaddle Mountain at 12:00 is capped by Hickory Sandstone.

12.8 County Road (CR) 308 to right to Honey Creek Cemetery and south to Red Mountain. Highway intersection is at the top of the Valley Springs Gneiss. Please see the separate road log and detailed map from this point to Red Mountain.

Road Log to Red Mountain

0.0 Texas Highway 71 and CR 308. Intersection is at the top of the Valley Springs Gneiss and base of the Packsaddle Schist. As we travel south on CR 308 we will cross the entire Packsaddle Schist section.

0.1 Outcrops of lower unit of Packsaddle Schist. Lithologies include graphite, hornblende and muscovite schists , leptite (metamorphosed rhyolite) and marble.

0.8 Honey Creek. Massive outcrops upstream are marble.

1.6 Y, take south fork (left).

4.8 Cattle guard. End of pavement. Now near the middle of the Packsaddle Schist group. Linear hill to east is a sill of Red Mountain Gneiss.

7.7 Junction with CR 310, keep right. Now on schists of the upper part of the Packsaddle Schist group.

8.1 Small stream valley. Metamorphosed mafic igneous rock is exposed west of the road.

8.5 Ford through Sandy Creek. There are sills of Red Mountain Gneiss on either side of the creek. Bureau of Economic Geology Guidebook 13 (Barnes, 1972) has a stop on the north side of the creek. To the west is a low hill underlain by another thick sill of Red Mountain Gneiss. To the east are low knobs of breccia, some of which exhibit cylindrical holes in which Indians ground corn.

9.0 Prominent ridge to the west is gneissic granite, the western continuation of the main sill of Red Mountain. It has been offset by a Precambrian strike-slip fault of about 600 feet. The fault produced a wide breccia zone lying approximately under CR 308.

9.1 Everett Ranch Gate.

9.4 Entrance to Red Mountain Ranch. Red Mountain is the high hill to the east. Bureau of Economic Geology Guidebook Number 13 has Stop 2 at this point (page 53). At the time this was the A.D. Hardin Ranch and they had permission to walk east to Comanche Creek. There the Packsaddle Schist is in fault contact with augen gneiss. End of log on CR 308.

CR 308 ends at the junction with FM 3347 at 13.0 miles. Return to junction CR 308 and 310

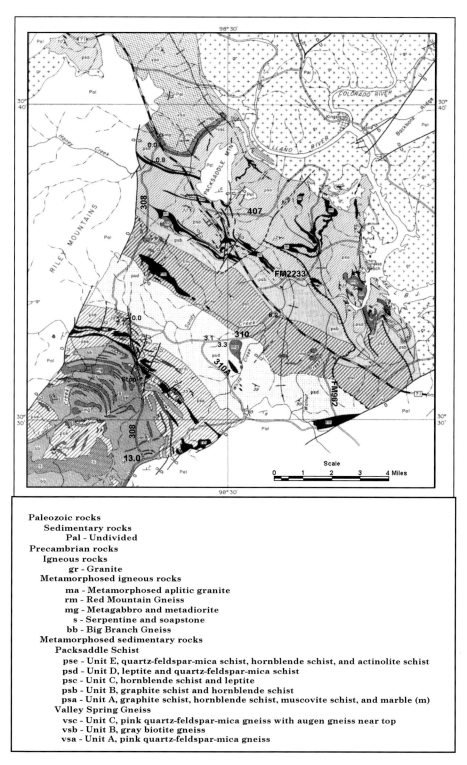

Paleozoic rocks
    Sedimentary rocks
        Pal - Undivided
Precambrian rocks
    Igneous rocks
        gr - Granite
    Metamorphosed igneous rocks
          ma - Metamorphosed aplitic granite
          rm - Red Mountain Gneiss
          mg - Metagabbro and metadiorite
          s - Serpentine and soapstone
          bb - Big Branch Gneiss
    Metamorphosed sedimentary rocks
        Packsaddle Schist
          pse - Unit E, quartz-feldspar-mica schist, hornblende schist, and actinolite schist
          psd - Unit D, leptite and quartz-feldspar-mica schist
          psc - Unit C, hornblende schist and leptite
          psb - Unit B, graphite schist and hornblende schist
          psa - Unit A, graphite schist, hornblende schist, muscovite schist, and marble (m)
        Valley Spring Gneiss
          vsc - Unit C, pink quartz-feldspar-mica gneiss with augen gneiss near top
          vsb - Unit B, gray biotite gneiss
          vsa - Unit A, pink quartz-feldspar-mica gneiss

Llano Uplift Figure 16 is from Barnes, et al, 1972, p.11. It has been modified to identify and post mileages on side roads. This is the type area of the Packsaddle Schist and the overlying metamorphosed igneous rocks. The road log covers CR 308 from Texas Highway 71 to the Red Mountain Ranch and a return route on CR 310 to Texas Highway 71. The county roads have a dirt base and the creeks have paved fords. These are strictly fair weather roads.

LU Figure 17. Looking northeast at type section of Red Mountain Gneiss.

0.0   Travel East on CR 310. In upper schist unit of Packsaddle Schist.

0.2   Ford

0.7   Cattle Guard.

1.4   Sandy Creek. Now on "d" unit of Packsaddle Schist (leptite and quartz-feldspar-mica schist).

2.9   Crossing Rough Ridge, an elongate hill of quartz-feldspar rock with subordinate hornblende and mica.

3.1   Junction with CR 310A.

3.3   Road cuts near stream are outcrops of Unit d

3.4   Green Mountain is south of the road. This is a large hill of amphibolite, a metamorphosed gabbro or diorite.

5.4   Ford. White Creek. In "C" unit.

5.6   Cattle Guard. Roadbed is on black hornblende schist.

6.2   Junction Texas Highway 71. This is mile point 20.7.

End of Red Mountain Road Logs

Continuation of Texas Highway 71 Road Log at junction with CR 308

13.4 Hill at 11:00 is Packsaddle Mountain. It is capped by Hickory Sandstone and Cap Mountain Limestone. The surrounding rocks are Packsaddle Schist.

13.9 Schist

14.3 Muscovite schist

14.5 Historical Marker. Two rocks are both quartz.

14.8 Schist

15.1 The Hickory Sandstone in Packsaddle Mountain looks like it fills a valley on the Precambrian surface.

15.7 CR 407 to left.

16.6 Schist

19.2 FM 2233 to left to Sunset Beach.

20.2 Road cut in weathered hornblende schist.

20.3 Sandy Creek. The sand along this creek is reported to be laced with fine particles of gold.

20.5 Roadside Picnic area on northeast side of road, CR 310 to west. This is the eastern road into the Red Mountain area. Watch for bears (TDPS) in this area!

22.4 Walnut Creek. Massive rock in creek bed is part of Packsaddle Schist section.

22.6 Round Mountain Road to south, FM 962.

23.8 FM 2831 to northeast.

25.2 Packsaddle Schist just west of creek on upthrown side of a northeast trending fault.

25.7 Lower part of Ellenburger Formation east of creek and fault. As we travel uphill we will be going up through the Ellenburger section.

26.4 Top of hill. Where the topography flattens beyond the top of the hill the dip is generally to the northeast so the highway is approximately along strike. For the next eight miles the highway is on weathered Ellenburger outcrops with a very thin soil. The outcrops usually look moth-eaten and filled in with red clay because of the partial solution of the limestone.

28.1 County Line Llano/Burnet

30.6 Every outcrop along this stretch of highway shows the corroded top of the Ellenburger Formation.

31.9 US Highway 281.

34.9 Entrance to Doublehorn Creek Ranch. Llano Uplift Figure 18 is a detailed map of this area. Please note this is private land. Just east of this entrance there is a north-south fault on the west side of a graben. The east side of the graben is a fault where the highway crosses Doublehorn Creek. The bedrock under the highway across the graben is Pennsylvanian Marble Falls Limestone.

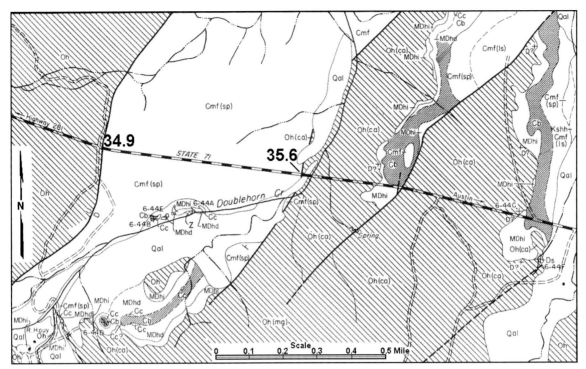

Llano Uplift Figure 18. Please see LU Figure 15 for location of this map. This figure shows Stop 8 from Bureau of Economic Geology Guidebook Number 13 (Barnes, 1972, p.61). The stop is on private land and permission is needed for entrance. The figure shows a number of small exposures of rocks between the top of the Ellenburger and the base of the Marble Falls. The interval represented is from Early Ordovician to Early Pennsylvanian time, about 300 million years. In various parts of the Llano Uplift at or overlying this unconformity there are fossils in: (1) fillings of sinkholes on the Ellenburger surface; (2) pebbles in conglomerates and regoliths (old soils); and (3) small remnant outcrops of formations that once covered the area. These clues to what once occurred here allow some insight to the history of deposition and erosion over the Llano Uplift area. For more details please see Barnes, et al, 1972.

35.6   Doublehorn Creek

35.7   Ellenburger Carbonates with east dip.

35.8   LU Figure 21 shows a fault here with Devonian rocks capped by Burnett Shale and Marble Fall Limestone on the west side (north of highway) of the fault and Ellenburger Carbonates on the east.

37.5   Quarry to south is in Ellenburger Formation.

38.4   Road to south. This point is the northwest edge of Cretaceous outcrops.

40.2   Cypress Creek. The northwest edge of the Edwards Group (Lower Cretaceous Limestones) is on the east side of this valley.

40.8   Spur 191. We are now on the Edwards Limestone.

End of Road Log.

Chapter 4
Permian Basin

The geologic history of the Permian Basin is fascinating because over a period of 300 million years the perfect succession of geologic events described in this chapter resulted in one of the major oil and gas producing provinces of the world. The Permian Basin comprises an area of about 120,000 square miles (300,000 square kilometers).

As shown on Ouachita Figure 3 The Permian Basin is one of a family of basins and uplifts across southern and western United States that **formed because of differential movements of the North American plate from Late Mississippian to Early Permian time.** The cause of the tectonism was discussed in the Ouachita Trend Chapter.

The Permian Basin, like many other basins and uplifts on Ouachita Figure 3, **developed over an older Cambrian to Middle Mississippian broad basin. The earlier basin of West Texas, the Tabosa Basin, extended from the Llano Uplift to west of El Paso, Texas.** The Tabosa Basin was the site of carbonate and clastic sedimentation that has been important in the production of oil and gas.

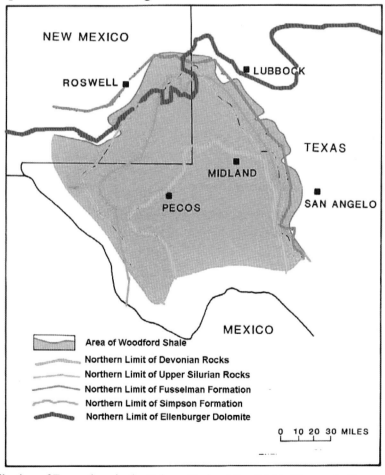

PB Figure 1. Distribution of Formations in the Tabosa Basin. After Ed McGlasson *in* Hanson and others, 1991.

The relative thickness of the sedimentary section over the Permian Basin is shown on PB Figure 2. Also shown are the major subdivisions of the basin. Some of these subdivisions are structural, such as the Diablo and Central Basin Platforms; others, such as the Eastern and Northwestern Shelves, are the result of carbonate and clastic shelf deposition marginal to arches to the east and northwest.

The Delaware, Midland, and Val Verde Basins of the Permian Basin were the sites of sediment deposited in deep water from Late Mississippian to early Permian time. **After that time, basin wide down warp of the basins and the uplifts occurred** and the entire area was progressively buried and filled in by the end of the Permian.

After the end of the Paleozoic Era, there was essentially no tectonic activity over the Permian Basin until middle Tertiary time when the whole West Texas area was involved in a broad, regional uplift and tilted to the east. The Salt Flat Graben rift sunk at that time along part of the west edge of the Delaware Basin.

The Tabosa Basin

Down warp of the Tabosa Basin started in the Cambrian and continued through the Middle Mississippian time. During this span of Paleozoic time, the Tabosa Basin was located in the subtropics within 30 degrees of the Equator. The dominant rock type deposited was shelf carbonate (limestone and dolomite; shelf carbonates and reefs are only deposited in warm water and are always within 30 degrees of the equator). During the Upper Ordovician, there was an extended period of clastic deposition that included two economically important sandstone intervals. Probably the most important sediment of the Tabosa Basin was the Late Devonian-Early Mississippian Woodford Shale. This unit is usually less that 100 feet thick, but is a very important source bed for oil and gas and seal for oil and gas traps.

As shown on Introduction Figure 1, periods of marine inundation alternated with times of erosion. The times of erosion are especially important as solution and karst topography was developed in the upper part of several of the carbonate sequences. The porosity and caves associated with the karst greatly enhanced those sections as reservoirs of oil and gas.

The following discussion is an overview of the sediments of the Tabosa Basin. A more comprehensive treatment is provide by chapters contributed by Hanson and others, 1991 and Frenzel and others, 1988 to the Geological Society of America *Decade of North American Economic Geology* Volume P-2 and *Geology of North America* Volume D-2.

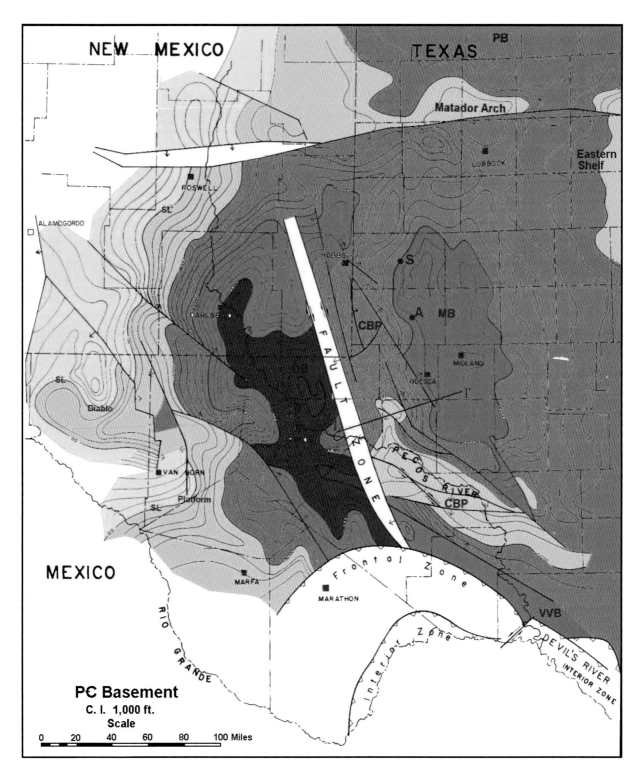

PB Figure 2. Present configuration of the Precambrian basement surface. DB=Delaware Basin. CBP=Central Basin Platform. MB=Midland Basin. VVB=Val Verde Basin (after Hills, 1982, p90).

Little is known about the Cambrian sediments of the Tabosa Basin as deep wells usually terminate in the upper part of the Ellenburger Dolomite. The section is probably similar to that surrounding the Llano Uplift.

The **Ellenburger Dolomite**, of Late Cambrian-Early Ordovician age, is over 1,500 feet (500 m) thick near the center of the basin. Erosion of the Ellenburger, whether pre-Simpson or later, resulted in widespread karst development and enlargement of the natural fracture system. The result is a section that usually has excellent reservoir characteristics and often is the main target in oil and gas exploration.

Near the center of the basin the overlying Ordovician **Simpson section** is over 2,000 feet (700 m) of green to gray shale. Over the southern part of the Central Basin Platform, three sandstones near the base are good reservoirs for oil and gas. The section has a distribution similar to that of the Ellenburger with the thickest section in south Pecos County. The source of these sediments is unknown.

The thickness of the **Late Ordovician Montoya through Devonian carbonates** generally total about 1,200 feet (400 m). There is a period of exposure and erosion after deposition of the Silurian **Fusselman Formation**. In the upper part of the Devonian, thick cherts appear to correlate with part of the Caballos silica beds of the Ouachita Trend. Over the Tabosa Basin, the Devonian cherts are naturally brecciated (broken up) and have good porosity.

After deposition of the Devonian chert, the Tabosa Basin was tilted southward and the northern ends of all formations from the Ordovician Ellenburger to the Devonian were progressively exposed and truncated. This was a period of widespread erosion that **created a low angle unconformity** at the base of the Woodford Shale.

Near the end of Devonian and continuing into early Mississippian time, essentially continent-wide deposition of black organic-rich shale occurred. In the Tabosa Basin it is the **Woodford Shale** section. This shale is more widespread than the underlying Silurian and Devonian rocks and in some area overlies much of the Ordovician section. In all areas the Woodford Shale is an important source bed and seal. A number of oil fields in the Midland Basin produce from Devonian, Upper Silurian, and Fusselman reservoirs where they subcrop the Woodford Shale.

Permian Basin Table 1.
Stratigraphic column of the Permian Basin and identification
of reservoir rocks (R), source rocks (SR), and seals (S).

	System	Series	Formation	Seal,Reservoir,Source
Permian Basin Sediments	Permian	Ochoa	Dewey Lake	S
			Rustler Limestone	R
			Salado	
			Castile	S
		Guadalupe	Tansill	
			Yates Sandstone	R
			Seven Rivers	S
			Queen Sandstone	R
			Grayburg	R
			San Andres Dolomite	R
		Leonard	Glorieta	R
			Clearfork	R
			Wichita-Albany	R
		Wolfcamp	Wolfcamp	R,S,SR
	Pennsylvanian	Virgil	Cisco	R,S,SR
		Missouri	Canyon	R,S,SR
		Des Moines	Strawn	R,S,SR
		Atoka	Atoka (Bend)	R,S,SR
		Morrow	Morrow	R,S,SR
	Mississippian	Chester	Barnett	R,S,SR
		Meremec	Barnett	
Tabosa Basin Sediments		Osage	Mississippian Limestone	R
		Kinderhook	Mississippian Limestone/Woodford Shale	S,SR
	Devonian	Undivided	Thirtyone Limestone	R
	Silurian	Upper	Wristen	SR
		Lower	Fusselman Limestone	R
	Ordovician	Upper	Montoya	R
		Middle	Simpson	R, S, SR
		Lower	Ellenburger Dolomite	R
	Cambrian	Upper	Hickory Sandstone	R

Permian Basin Formation and Filling

The structures of the Permian Basin, including basins, uplifts, faults, and anticlines developed in a series of tectonic pulses. The major pulses were: Middle Mississippian, early Morrowan, early Atokan, middle Desmoinesian, and early Wolfcampian. Most of these tectonic pulses also occur in nearby Late Paleozoic basins.

Paleogeographic reconstructions place the Permian Basin about 20 degrees south of the equator in the late Mississippian and gradually moving south. The basin was on the equator in mid-Pennsylvanian time and the region was about 15 degrees north by the end of the Permian.

Mississippian. The formation of the Permian Basin started in late Mississippian time. The first deposits were widespread marine muds of the **Barnett Shale**. The Barnett overlies lower Mississippian through Ellenburger rocks on a low relief angular unconformity.

Pennsylvanian

The sediments of the Pennsylvanian age **Morrow Formation** (PB Figure 3) are fine-grained sandstone and shales eroded from areas north, east, and northwest of the Delaware Basin. Down warp of the Delaware Basin is obvious. The rest of the Permian Basin was exposed to erosion and were most likely low rolling hills at this time.

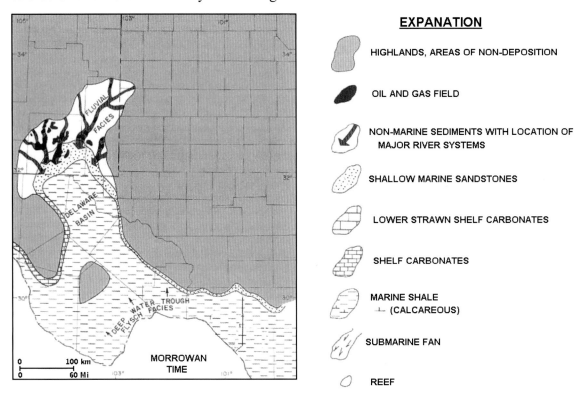

PB Figure 3. Morrowan paleogeographic map showing early downwarp of the Delaware Basin and Morrow sediments fed from the north. After Hanson and others, 1991. Explanation covers PB Figures 3 to 7.

The sediments of **Atoka age** (PB Figure 4) record widespread changes in the paleogeography in response to the tectonic forces that are creating the surrounding highlands and deepening the basins. Clastic sedimentation is replaced by shelf limestones in the northern part of the Delaware Basin. River systems from rising highlands of the Wichita Mountains to the northeast and Ouachita Trend to the east bring coarse conglomerates and sandstones of the **Bend Formation** to the northeast part of the newly formed Midland Basin. The deep-water shales and limestones of the Haymond and Dimple Formations of the Marathon region primarily came from a source southeast of the deep-water trough.

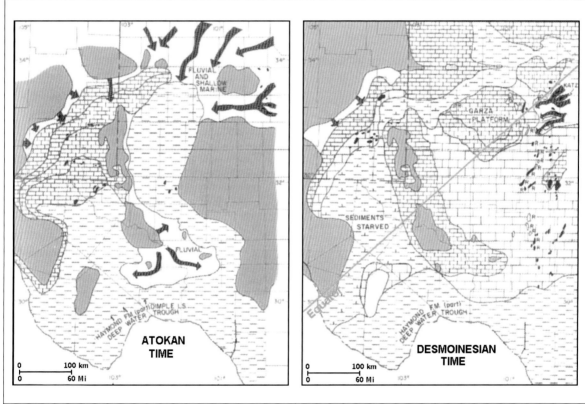

PB Figure 4. Atokan paleogeographic map showing the down warp of the Midland Basin and early uplift of the Central Basin Platform area (after Hanson and others, 1991).

PB Figure 5. Composite of early and late Desmoinsian (lower and upper Strawn) paleogeographic maps showing basin wide establishment of uplifts and shelf margins. Reefs begin to grow in and around the Midland Basin. Deeper parts of basins are "sediment starved" (after Hanson and others, 1991).

58

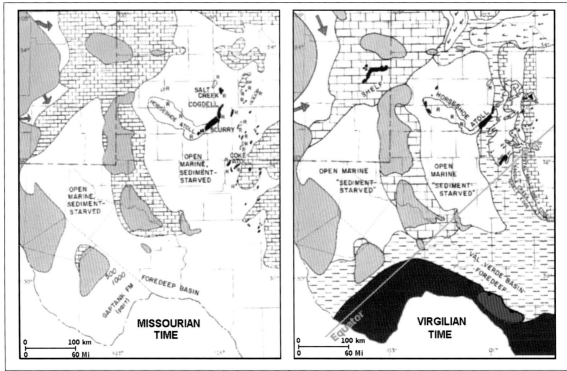

PB Figure 6. Missourian (Canyon Formation) paleogeographic map. After Hanson and others, 1991.	PB Figure 7. Virgilian (Cisco Formation) paleogeographic map showing platform and shelf relationships that persisted through Permian time. Filling of "sediment-starved" basins began in earliest Permian time and was completed by the end of the Permian. After Hanson and others, 1991.

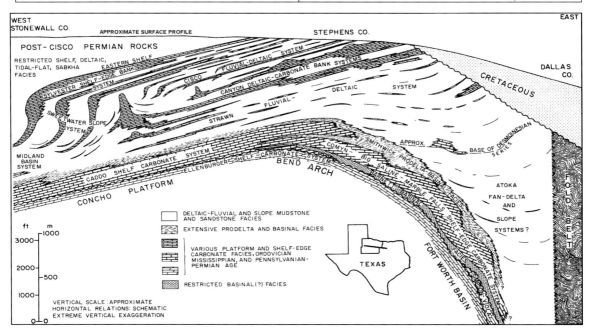

PB Figure 8. Early and Middle Pennsylvanian cyclothemic depositional systems from the Forth Worth Basin to the northeast part of the Midland Basin. It is apparent that the Ouachita Fold Belt to the east is being actively eroded and that the clastics from that source were filling the Forth Worth Basin. Essentially no clastics were being transported to the Midland Basin (from Brown, et al, 1987).

The paleogeography of **Desmoinesian (lower and upper Strawn) time** (PB Figure 5) shows considerable changes. Current reconstructions of the North American plate during Pennsylvanian time have the continent oriented about 45 degrees clockwise from the current north and place the **equator** through Midland, Texas and extending through the southern Great Lakes and out the Saint Lawrence seaway. **The Permian Basin must have been a tropical paradise**.

The Delaware and Midland basins continue to deepen, but are isolated from areas being actively eroded. As a result, there is widespread deposition of shelf limestones around the edges of the basins, while only very thin limestone or **no deposition of sediment** occurred across the middle of the basins. The basins are described as being **"starved"** of clastic sediments. The Desmoinesian was the time of formation of relatively small linear reefs along the east side of Midland Basin and the beginning of development of the **Horseshoe Reef,** around the edges of the Garza Platform in the northern part of the Midland Basin.

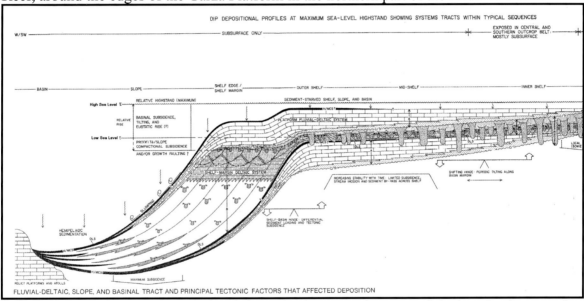

PB Figure 9. Development of a typical cyclothem. As shown, equal amounts of clastic and carbonate rocks were deposited. Variations from this ideal depend of the amount of clastics available for transport across the carbonate shelves and the length of each part of the cyclothem (from Brown, et al, 1987).

During the Pennsylvanian and most of the Permian, sea level fluctuated up and down in a **cyclical fashion** in response to the extent of widespread glaciation in the southern hemisphere. During glacial periods sea level dropped 200 to 400 feet, and subaerial drainage was developed over the carbonate shelf deposits. Streams transported clastic sands and muds that built deltas across and basinward of the previous carbonate shelf edge. The interglacial times of high sea level were times of reef building and shelf limestone deposition. **This cyclical pattern of sea level fluctuation and resulting alternation of clastic deposition during low sea levels and carbonate deposition during high stands continued throughout Pennsylvanian time and most of the Permian Period.**

The Missourian, Virgilian and Wolfcampian (early Permian) epochs were a continuation of late Strawn deposition. During all of this time the reefs of the Midland Basin grew taller as the basin subsided. Both the Delaware and Midland basins remained starved for clastic sediments until late in Virgilian time. By that time, high stand limestone shelf edges had prograded across the Fort Worth Basin and Bend Arch and into the eastern part of the Midland Basin. During low sea level stands, clastic sediment resulted in the formation of deltas along the east edge of the Midland Basin. Down slope from the deltas, deposition of submarine fans sometimes wrapped around the reefs. The muds of the fans were good source beds that, with burial and compaction, fed oil and gas to both the sandstones of the fans and the reefs.

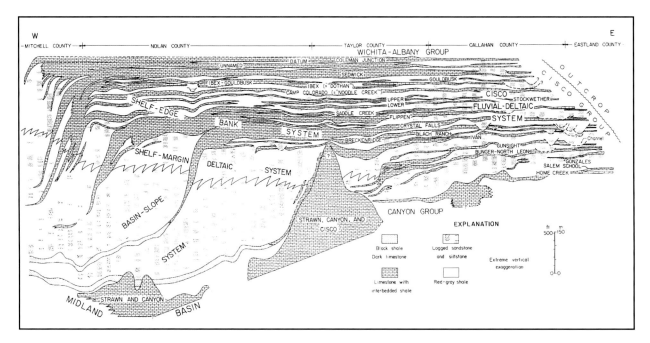

PB Figure 10. Generalized dip cross-section of Late Pennsylvanian and Early Permian rocks across North-Central Texas. The cyclothemic fluctuations of sea level average about 300 feet between low and high stands. The basinward progradation of the shelf edges continues from that shown on PB Figure 8. This reconstruction has a datum at the top of the Coleman Junction Formation (top of Wolfcampian). Because of down warping and sediment loading, the Midland Basin continued to subside during the time shown so that the entire section is tilted to the west in the same manner as the west half of PB Figure 8 (from Brown, et al, 1987).

During the Virgilian, the mountain building of the Ouachita Trend extended into the Marathon Region. Sediments, especially mud, eroded from these rising mountains contributed thick sections of shale to the Val Verde and Marfa Basins.

Horseshoe Atoll

Comparison of Permian Basin Figures 5 to 7 and 11 shows a large ninety-five by eighty mile platform developed in the northern part of the Midland Basin in early Desmoinesian time. By the end of the Desmoinesian, reefs developed along three sides forming a large horseshoe pattern. The feature was right on the equator. The reason for the initial formation of the platform may have been a response to currents around the north end of the basin. Plate tectonic reconstructions, including work by Walker, et al (1991), show a northeast orientation of the continent at that time. The present southeast side of the platform was the south side at time of deposition.

The Horseshoe Reef is a classic example of an ancient carbonate atoll. Widespread erosional disconformities in the Lower Strawn (early Desmoinesian) section indicate periodic cyclothemic exposure of the platform. The thin black marine shales above each unconformity are probable reworked soils. After Lower Strawn deposition, the Horseshoe Reef grew as a series of isolated carbonate mounds and pinnacles. The nature of subsequent reef growth suggests that the main growth took place during high sea level stands. The reefs were true bioherms with facies distribution of successive layers controlled by the prevailing trade winds. From windward to leeward, the facies changed from oolitic to algal-sponge-bryozoan limestones to tidal flat limestones with algal mounds.

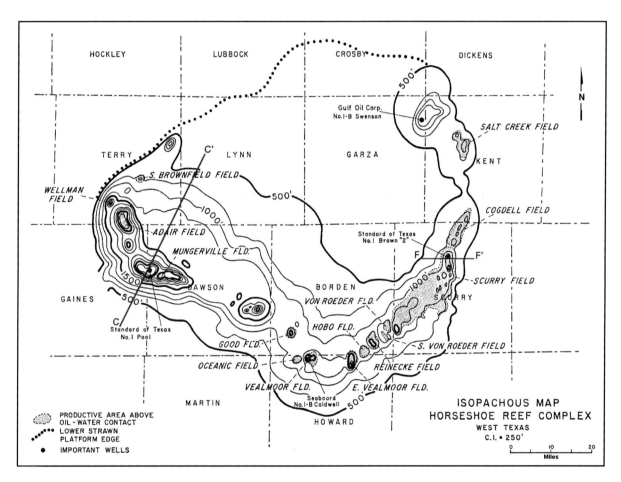

PB Figure 11. Isopach map of Horseshoe reef complex showing location of significant production from reef limestones along the crest of the atoll (from Vest, 1970).

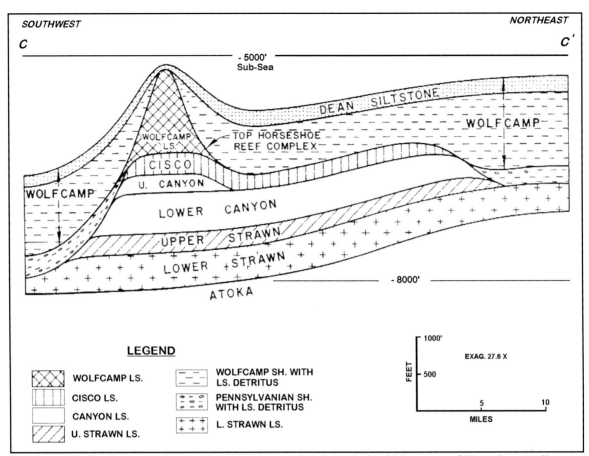

PB Figure 12. Southwest-northeast schematic cross section through the thickest part of Horseshoe Atoll. Location of section is shown on PB Figure 11 (from Vest, 1970).

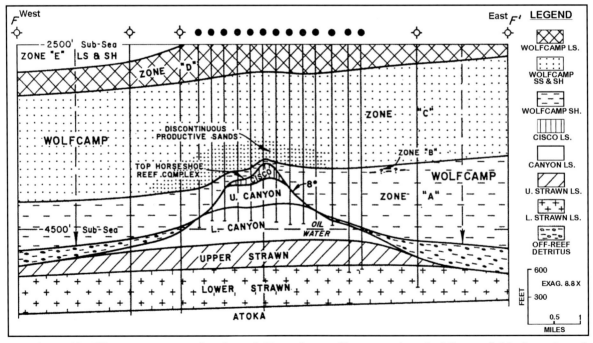

PB Figure 13. West-east cross section through Horseshoe atoll near north end of Scurry field. Location of section is shown on PB Figure 11 (from Vest, 1970).

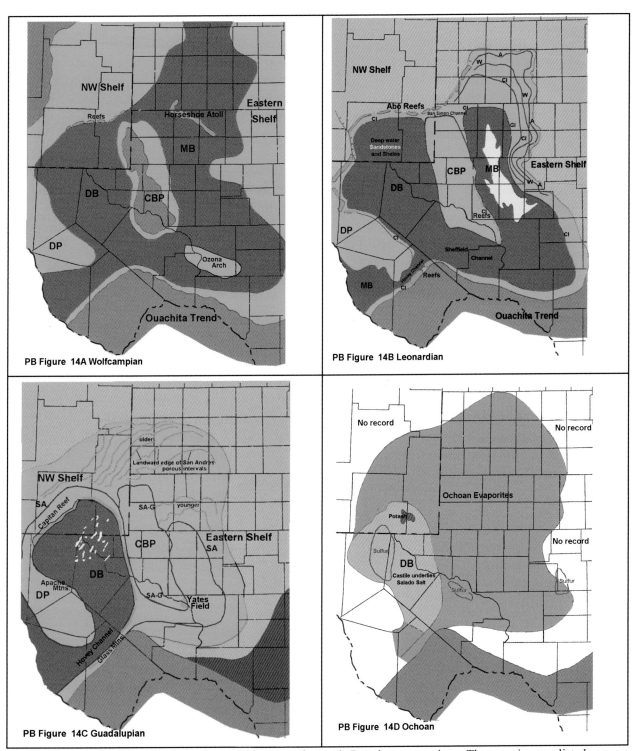

PB Figure 14. Summary paleogeographic maps for each Permian age series. These series are listed on Permian Basin Table 1, page 55. On each map DP=Diablo Platform, DB=Delaware Basin, CBP=Central Basin Platform, and MB=Midland Basin. On Figure 14B, the location of the Leonardian shelf edges of the following formations is posted: A=Abo, W=Wichita, Cl=Clearfork, and Gl=Glorieta. On Figure 14C, the carbonate shelf edge at the end of San Andres-Grayburg deposition is labeled Sa and Sa-G. The landward edges of important cyclothems of Guadalupian age are shown (see discussion on page 68). The yellow bars in the Delaware Basin on this map indicate the position of oil fields that produce from sandstones deposited in deep water.

By late Cisco time, prograding muds from the eastern shelf covered the eastern part of the Horseshoe. The muds stopped all growth of the eastern part, but the areas farther west were in clear water and continued to grow through Cisco and lower Wolfcampian time. By middle Wolfcamp time, all parts of the Garza Platform and the atoll reefs were buried in organic-rich muds. Subsequent burial of the entire area as the Midland Basin was filled insured that the oil and gas generated in the muds would migrate into the reefs. The muds also provided the seal that kept the hydrocarbons in this gigantic trap.

Oil accumulation in the atoll reefs is not uniform. The basin subsided more and basin filling was thicker to the west. Thus the entire platform and reef complex is tilted to the west. The largest field on the atoll is the Scurry Field with cumulative production of more than 1.1 billion barrels of oil from an oil column of 765 feet (Vest, 1970). Ultimate yield is estimated as 1.3 billion barrels of oil. Total ultimate production for the atoll is estimated at 2.4 billion barrels of oil from 15 fields (Galloway, et al, 1983). Drilling depths are 6,300 to 9,300 feet.

Permian

Wolfcampian

The Permian Period started as a continuation of the sedimentation of the Virgilian Epoch, but **shortly after the beginning of the period the whole region was subjected to major tectonic activity. The basins were deepened and the Central Basin and Diablo Platforms underwent their final and greatest amount of uplift and structuring.** At this same time, the final emplacement of the overthrust sheets of the Ouachita Trend took place. The combination suggests that the termination of the docking of North America with the microcontinents of the Gulf of Mexico area occurred in one final bang and then there was an end of all tectonic movements. **During the rest of the Permian Period, the whole Permian Basin region subsided as the basins were completely filled. Eventually the whole area, including the uplifts, was buried by an average of 5,000 feet of Permian sediments.**

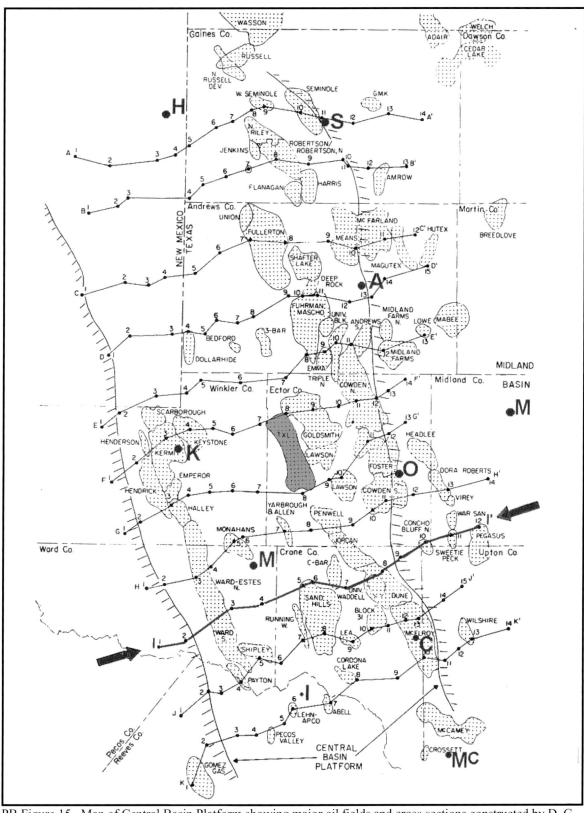

PB Figure 15. Map of Central Basin Platform showing major oil fields and cross sections constructed by D. G. Bebout and K. J. Meador, 1985. Please note location of Cross Section I - I' (PB Figure 16) and TXL Field (PB Figure 28). Initials indicate the location of key towns.

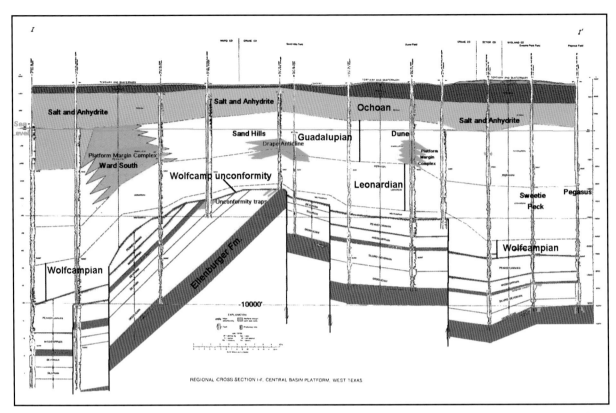

PB Figure 16. West-East cross section I - I' across Central Basin Platform. Please note the major angular unconformity at the base of the Wolfcamp strata. Location of cross section is highlighted on PB Figure 19. Bright green is posted to show major oil and gas reservoirs (after Bebout and Meador, 1985).

The upper part of PB Figure 16 illustrates that by middle Wolfcampian time the uplifted areas of the Central Basin Platform were deeply eroded and were being progressively drowned as the whole basin underwent gradual subsidence. Cyclical sedimentation on the Eastern Shelf of the Midland Basin and the Northwest Shelf of the Delaware Basin continued throughout the Wolfcampian with no indication of the early Wolfcampian tectonic activity in those areas.

Leonardian

The type section for the Leonardian Epoch is located at Leonard Mountain in the middle of the Glass Mountains. Shelf carbonates prograded from the northwest edge of the Marathon Mountains.

There was a complete change of climate after the Wolfcampian. From the start of the Leonardian to the end of the Permian this part of the continent had moved far enough north of the equator to be in the horse latitudes (above 15 degrees north) where desert conditions prevail over land areas, and shallow water areas (lagoons and salt pans) are the sites of extensive evaporation. From this time on shelf carbonates and reefs dominated the edges of the basins. Landward, the lagoonal areas were sabkhas; that is, areas of evaporate sedimentation. Inland from the lagoons the clastics are red beds and wide spread sand dunes are common. Locally, like around Sweetwater, Texas thick gypsum deposits of the sabkha

environment are economically exploited.   Thick salt deposits of Leonardian and
Guadalupian age extend north from the Permian Basin across the Palo Duro Basin and far
north into western Kansas (Wolfcampian carbonates that underlie the salts are the reservoir
sections of the very large Panhandle Gas Field).

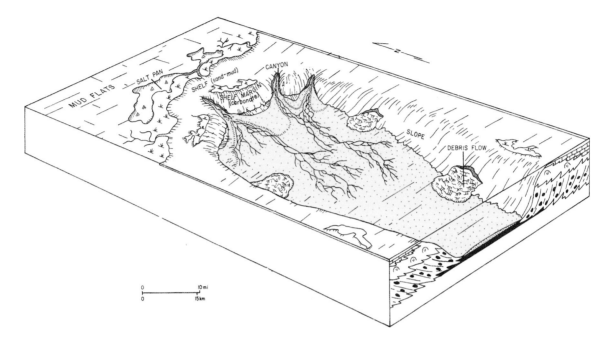

PB Figure 17. Deposition of the deep water Dean and Spraberry Sandstones the length of the Midland Basin
during Leonardian time. From Galloway, et al, 1983.

The **shelf edges of major units of the Leonardian** are posted on Permian Basin Figure
14B. The carbonate shelf edges continued to prograde basinward and in combination with
the clastic part of each cyclothem, were progressively filling the basins in a massive landfill
manner. Thick clastic sections were deposited across the broad basins in water depths of
several thousand feet (PB Figure 17). The sediments included important sandstone
reservoirs and shale source beds. This distribution of carbonates and clastics continued to
end of the Guadalupian when the Capitan Reef was the final shelf edge carbonate.

Guadalupian

The paleogeography of the Guadalupian was much like that of the Leonardian except that
the shelf carbonates of the San Andres and Grayburg Formations were much wider.
The San Andres-Grayburg carbonate section includes at least twelve cyclothems that are
recorded by progradation of individual carbonate intervals. Widespread dolomitization of
the shelf carbonates added about seven percent to the porosity and resulted in excellent
reservoirs for oil and gas. The **landward limits** of the carbonates of each cycle across the
northwest shelf and Midland Basin are posted on PB Figure 14C. The reason for posting
landward limits rather than shelf edges is that the individual reservoirs of each cycle are
thick and (1) sealed updip by facies change to sabkhas sediments and (2) were overlain by
the evaporites of the succeeding cycle. The total picture is one of a series of shingles that are

progressively younger to the south. **For much of the Permian Basin the San Andres-Grayburg carbonates were the <u>last widespread reservoir in the sedimentary sequence</u>. Oil and gas migrate towards the surface. Thus <u>these formations contain most of the oil in the basin</u>. There are many <u>giant</u> (over 100 million barrels produced) and <u>several mega-giant</u> (over one billion barrels) fields that produce from San Andres-Grayburg reservoirs. In total, San Andres-Grayburg fields have contributed over 60 percent of the 35 billion barrels of oil produced in the Permian Basin.**

The illustrations with the discussions of Yates Field, Central Basin Platform, Northwest Shelf and Deep Water Sands all show production from Guadalupian reservoirs. After the deposition of the Grayburg all areas except for the Delaware Basin were sabkhas and inland clastic domains. From the Grayburg on prograding reefs progressive constricted the edges of the Delaware Basin until the deposition of the basin circling **Capitan Reef** at the end of the Guadalupian.

Ochoan

The final stages of the Permian succession saw the deposition of evaporates everywhere across the basin. It was a time when **basin wide shallow water was periodically recharged with marine water** that brought new supplies of evaporite minerals. **It must have been an incredible terrain of desolation.** In the Delaware basin the first basin-filling evaporate section was primarily gypsum (Castile Formation), which converts to anhydrite with compaction. The next stage was widespread deposition of salt over the entire Permian Basin (Salado Salt in Delaware Basin, Ochoa Formation elsewhere). In the north-central part of Delaware Basin the evaporation was so severe that the **exotic potassium salt *sylvite*** was deposited in quantities that have been of commercial importance. The last Paleozoic marine event in the Permian Basin was the deposition of a 100 +/- feet thick dolomite over the Delaware Basin (**Rustler Dolomite**). Locally there are thin sections of red sandstones and shales of non-marine origin (Dewey Lake Redbeds) above the Rustler Dolomite that are the last Paleozoic sediments deposited in the Permian Basin.

PB Figure 18. Outcrop of Ochoan age Castile Gypsum in northwest part of Delaware Basin. The rhythmic bedding is believed to reflect annual increments (varves) of gypsum. The dark layers include dust. Young man is Derek Sturdavant.

Outcrops of Permian Reefs

Excellent exposures of Permian Reefs occur in the Guadalupe, Apache, and Glass Mountains of West Texas and southeast New Mexico. The most spectacular and the most easily visited and studied reefs are those of the Guadalupe Mountains. The Carlsbad Cavern and Guadalupe Mountain National Parks preserve the area and provide easy access. The Apache Mountains of the western part of the Delaware Basin are a short distance north of Interstate Highway 10 and are accessible by state and county roads. The Glass Mountains are beautiful to look at from a distance, but are entirely on private land in an area where permission is hard to come by.

The reefs of the Guadalupe and Apache Mountains are shelf edge features formed during the last events (**Capitan Reef**) of the normal marine flooding of the Delaware Basin. The Glass Mountains are comprised of a series of reefs that prograded northwest from the Marathon Mountains (at that time) toward the Hovey Channel. They range in age from late Wolfcampian to late Guadalupian.

Guadalupe Mountains

The **Guadalupe Mountain** rocks are those of a **very large and long barrier reef, the Capitan Reef. This type of barrier reef is very similar to the present day Great Australian and Belize Barrier Reefs.** The continuity of sediments down the slope into the basin facies are the best found anywhere in the world. In places like McKittrick Canyon it is an easy hike from rocks of the top of the reef to those deposited in the basin. Total relief between the reef and deeper parts of the basin is over 5,000 feet.

During the Miocene the Capitan Reef trend was uplifted and tilted to the east from the fault at the east side of the Salt Flat graben. All of the barrier reef is exposed at the west end. Northeastward it is still completely exposed at Carlsbad Cavern National Park and then continues into the subsurface until the whole barrier reef is buried at the west edge of Carlsbad, New Mexico.

Basinward from the reef front there are excellent exposures in road cuts along US Highways 62 and 180 of channels filled by turbidite sandstone and some debris flows (PB Figure 22). The courser clastics are all enclosed in marine shales. Many of the sandstones contain abundant small fossils called fusilinids (single-celled plankton organisms that look like wheat grains).

PB Figure 19. Looking north at southwest end of Guadalupe Mountains. The spectacular exposures are the result of erosion of the uplifted reef east of the Salt Flat graben. Close study of the light-colored limestone cliffs will reveal bedding planes that record the slope of successive stages of progradation. Locally the bedding planes can be traced (right) into the basinward clastics. Below the massive limestone the section is predominantly shale with distinct channels filled by turbidite sandstones. These sandstones make prominent ledges in the black shale section. Photograph was contributed by Jon Smith, Photographer; email jurysmith@msn.com.

PB Figure 20. Sketch of the stratigraphic relationships shown in PB Figure 19. From King, 1948, Plate 12. Please also see the interpretation of depositional relief and facies shown on PB Figure 26 in the discussion below of caves in the Guadalupe Mountains.

PB. Figure 21. Looking south of US Highways 62 and 180 neat Guadalupe Pass at exposures of channel sandstones (turbidites) interbedded with deep-water marines shales.

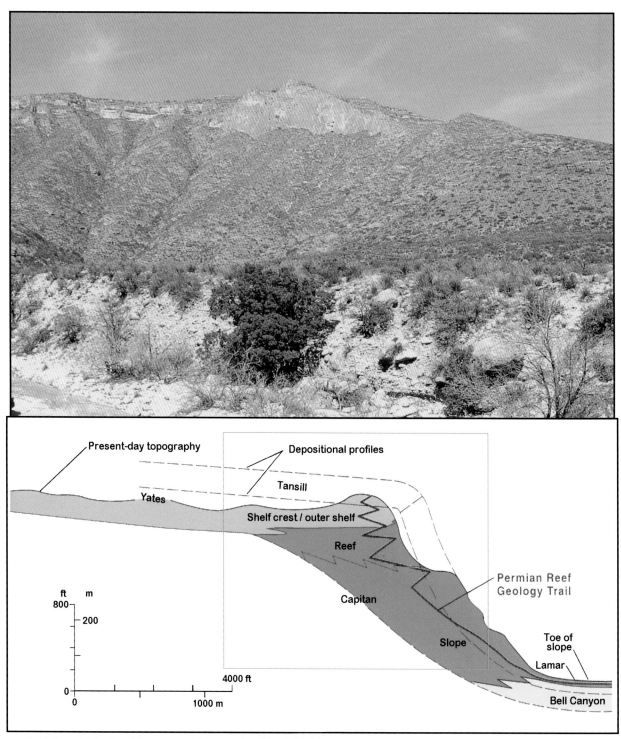

PB Figure 22. Looking across the mouth of McKittrick Canyon at the southeast edge of the Capitan Reef. There is a hiking trail from the visitor's center to the top of the reef that has signs that identify parts of the reef and contained fossils. The area of the picture is posted on the accompanying sketch cross section (from Bebout and Karens, 1993).

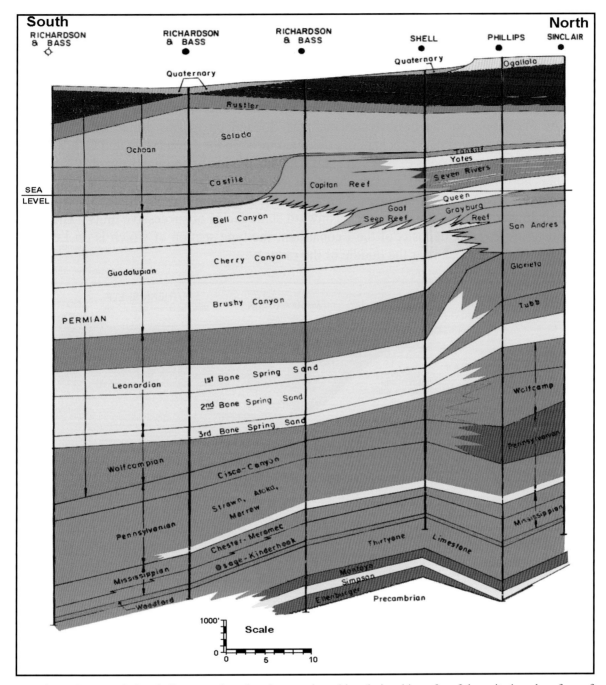

PB Figure 23. North-South Cross section showing stratigraphic relationships of reef deposits in subsurface of northern Delaware Basin (from Hills, 1985).

Apache Mountains

The Apache Mountains are on the uplifted area east of the Salt Flat Graben. The mountains are a large asymmetric anticline faulted on the west and northeast sides. The west end of the range is complexly faulted where the anticline intersects the fault system on the east side of the Salt Flat graben. The Capitan reef is exposed in the core of the range and on the northwest end. Along the southwest sides of the range back reef sabkha sediments and sand dunes intervals are exposed.

Glass Mountains

The Glass Mountains are located on the northwest flank of the Marathon Uplift. The last mountain-building activity in this part of the Ouachita Trend was during the early Permian (PB Figure 24). By Middle Wolfcampian time, the mountains were eroded to low hills, and by Late Wolfcampian the northwest flank was flooded by marine water and thin shelf carbonates were deposited. This pattern continued through the Leonardian and Guadalupian with successive narrow belts of reef and shelf deposits gradually building towards the Hovey Channel (northeast continuation of the Marfa Basin on PB Figure 24). There are excellent exposures of small reefs in the Glass Mountains. It is possible to walk laterally from the reef and down the upper slope into the basinward shale facies of successive units. The most prominent are the reef deposits of the Leonardian, the type section of which is on Leonard Mountain (the high peak near the middle of the range).

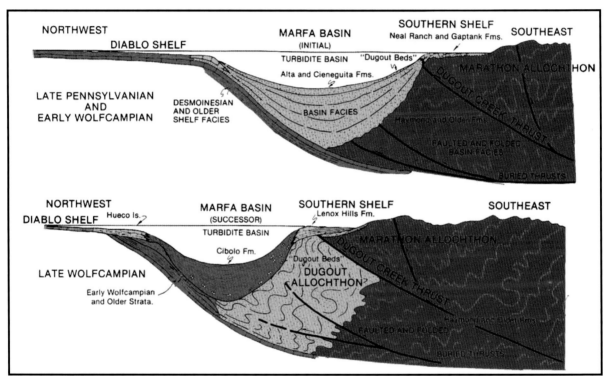

PP Figure 24. Cross-section illustrating the formation of Permian reefs (labeled Southern Shelf) on the northwest flank of the Marathon Mountains. After Ross and Ross, 1985.

Sulfur Deposits

The Ochoan Map, PB Figure 14D, shows three areas where elemental sulfur has been produced in the Permian Basin. In all three areas sulfur has been recovered using the Frasch process. Elemental sulfur has also been found in caves of the Guadalupe Mountains. Most have been small deposits, but those in Lechuguilla Cave are described as multi-ton massive deposits (Hill, 1996, p.356). The main producing area is the Rustler Springs sulfur district of the northern part of the Delaware Basin.

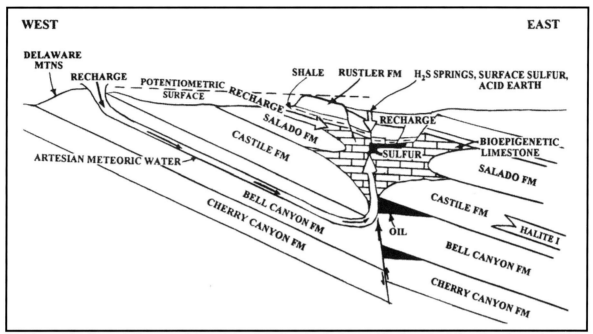

PB Figure 25. General diagram of the origin of the Rustler Springs sulfur deposit. Like oil and gas, the H2S that carries the sulfur has to have some sort of seal or it will escape to the surface. Here there is a clay layer that traps the H2S. From Hill, 1996.

In the Rustler Springs area a number of circumstances have combined to cause precipitation of sulfur.

1. The Castile Formation contains thick sections of anhydrite (CaSO4).
2. It is underlain by sandstones of the Delaware and Cherry Canyon Formations that provide an avenue for the movement of meteoric water down from outcrops to the west and for the migration of oil and gas up from source beds in the basin.
3. The front where the fresh and connate water meet (redox interface) is characterized by extensive solution of the overlying evaporites so that all the salt has been dissolved and part of the anhydrite. The anhydrite is also changed to gypsum (CaSO4.H2O). Solution caused collapse of the Castile beds and the development of avenues for vertical migration of fluids.
4. Bacteria that feed on hydrocarbons apparently play a role in the breakdown of the gypsum, the release of H2S gas into migrating water, and the deposition of elemental sulfur from the H2S gas.

It has been calculated that to produce the sulfur in the Culberson deposit, approximately 200 million barrels of oil or 3.6 trillion cubic feet of natural gas would be required, i.e., four barrels of oil to produce one ton of sulfur (Hill, 1995, p. 365). The age of the sulfur deposits has to be fairly recent, that is since the uplift of this area in the Miocene and contemporaneous with the erosion of the western part of the Delaware Basin.

At one time the Culberson sulfur mines in the Rustler Spring District were the largest Frasch-mining operation in the United States (Hill, 1996, p. 360). Sulfur is no longer produced. Apparently an over supply of sulfur around the world reduced the price to where it was no longer profitable to mine sulfur in the Delaware Basin.

Caves

Caves are formed in carbonate rocks by two methods. The most common is associated with the movement of meteoric waters downward from the surface to a ground water table some distance below the surface. Rainwater picks up carbon from decaying vegetation, making a weak carbonic acid that dissolves the $CaCO_3$ of the carbonate rocks. Mammoth Cave of Kentucky is an example. Calcite deposits of all types are characteristic of this type of cave.

Less common are caves that are developed below the ground water surface by the movement of H_2S-charged waters upward. The caves of the Guadalupe Mountains are of this type. H_2S released by the processes described in the Sulfur discussion combines with water to make sulfuric acid. This acid has been found in caves, sometimes in strong concentrations.

Some of the caves of the Guadalupe Mountains are very large and characterized by both abundant gypsum and calcite deposits. Lechuguilla Cave has been protected with a special entrance to keep outside air from circulating through the cave as it would dissolve and adversely affect the delicate gypsum crystal formations.

The caves of the southwestern part of the Guadalupe Mountains have been dated at 12 million years. Lechuguilla and Carlsbad Caverns are 3 million years old.

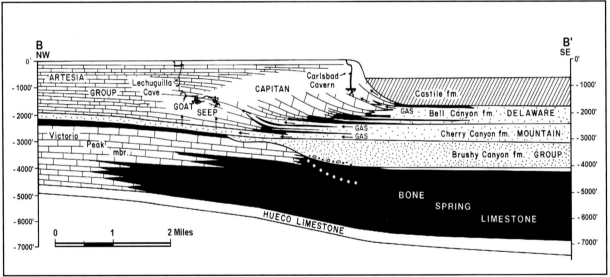

PB Figure 26. Possible avenues of hydrogen sulfide gas ascension to form Carlsbad Cavern and Lechuguilla Cave. From Hill, 1990, fig.8, p. 1692.

Oil and Gas

To preserve large quantities of oil and gas so that they can be explored and exploited, a basin must have ideal conditions regarding four controls. There must be (1) thick and organically rich source beds, (2) thick porous and permeable reservoirs beds, (3) many large traps along migrations routes and (4) effective seals for the traps so that the hydrocarbons do not escape to the surface.

(1) In the discussion of Paleozoic sediments thick black shales have been described in Ordovician, Devonian, Mississippian, Pennsylvanian, and Permian sediments. These shales are rich in the organic material that changes to oil and gas with burial to depths over 4,000 feet.

(2) During each of the Paleozoic periods, there were shelf areas around the basins where thick carbonates were deposited. Cyclical sedimentation occurred throughout the Paleozoic, so the carbonates were repeatedly exposed to erosion and the enhancement of porosity and permeability that are the result of subaerial erosion. During the Pennsylvanian and Permian, sea level fluctuations included low sea level stands when sands and muds were transported into the basins from surrounding highlands. The end result is many porous and permeable carbonate and sandstone reservoirs in all parts of the Permian Basin.

(3) Large traps include: unconformity traps at the base of the Devonian Woodford Shale; structures formed by the tectonic events from Late Mississippian to Early Wolfcamp time and structures in sediments that drape over them; stratigraphic traps in reefs, shelf carbonates, and every type of lenticular sand deposit imaginable.

(4) Thick **Ochoan evaporite sections that provide the seal over the Central Basin Platform and both basins** keep oil and gas from migrating to the surface. This seal puts the cap on ideal source, reservoir, and trap distribution and fortuitously makes **the Permian Basin one of the largest oil and gas producing areas in the world. Cumulative production is 35 billion barrels of oil and 98 trillion cubic feet of gas. In the United States, the Permian Basin is the source of over 20 percent of all domestic oil and gas.**

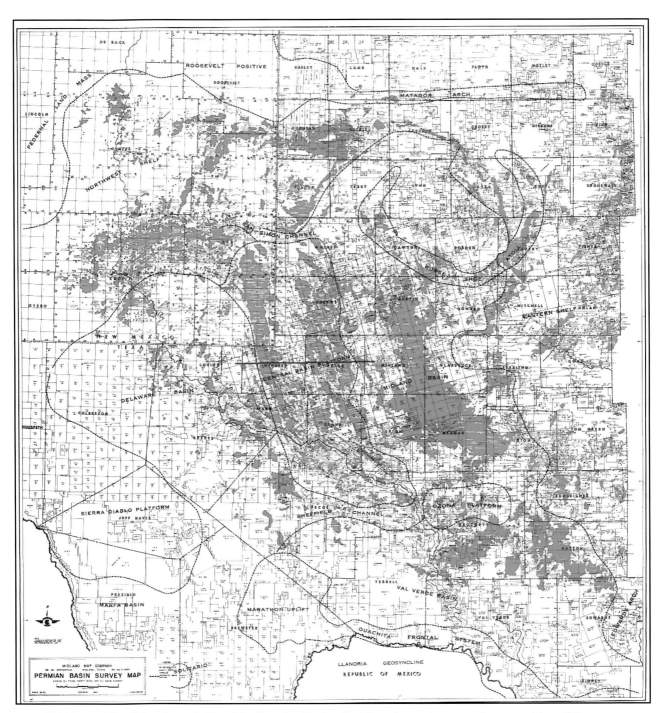

PB Figure 27.   Oil and gas fields of the Permian Basin. Red line shows the approximate position of the cross section on PB Figure 16 (reproduced with permission of the Midland Map Company).

Central Basin Platform

The **Central Basin trend is a 50-mile wide region between the Delaware and the Midland Basins characterized by many uplifted fault blocks.** Locally, there is over 20,000 feet (6,000 meters) of structural relief between the deepest part of the Delaware Basin and the high areas of the platform. The Central Basin structures were formed as the entire Permian Basin developed in Late Mississippian to early Permian (early Wolfcampian) time. The last pulse of structuring was by far the strongest and most defining event. **The uplifted area was deeply eroded and then <u>buried</u> by +/- 5,000 feet of shallow water deposits from the middle Wolfcampian to the end of Permian time.** Picture a structurally high area with many excellent reservoirs sections in both the eroded structured section and the draping, overlying platform rocks that were fed migrating oil and gas from the prolific shale source beds in Delaware and Midland basins. **This entire package was covered by late Permian evaporate deposits (anhydrite and salt) that formed a cap that effectively sealed the entire area and <u>did not allow any of the hydrocarbons to escape.</u>** This explains why there are many large oil fields over the entire the Central Basin area (PB Figures 15 and 16).

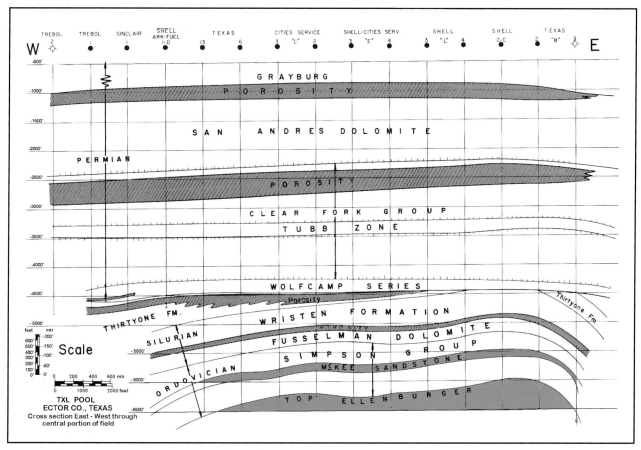

PB Figure 28. West-east cross sections of TXL Field (Green field on PB Figure 15). Production obtained from both the structured section below the early Wolfcamp unconformity and the shallower drape structure is highlighted (from Gallaway, 1983).

In the structured section below the Early Wolfcamp unconformity, oil is produced from fault traps, faulted anticlines, and unconformity traps. Some are shown on PB Figures 16 and 28. These same figures show fields developed in the post-unconformity section in the platform margin reef-like complexes. Several of these fields are giants that produced more than 100 million barrels of oil.

The fault blocks of the Central Basin region were developed in a series of tectonic pulses. Some faults terminate near the base of the Pennsylvanian section; others in the middle, and most terminate at the base of the middle Wolfcampian sediments. No fault extends above that point. Between early and middle Wolfcampian time, there was a short period of intense erosion and then the entire area subsided below sea level. The basins on either side subsided at a slightly faster rate (probably because of the additional weight of thicker sediment sections being deposited) so that the Central Basin region remained a platform to the end of Guadalupian time.

Many fields produce from drape anticlines. These features are formed by compaction of the sediments over buried hills at the Wolfcamp Unconformity. Some hills develop right over the structures as shown at Sand Hills on PB Figure 16 and the TXL field (PB Figure 28). Others, such as Penwell and Jordan fields, produce from early Paleozoic reservoirs in faulted anticline structures. They also produce at shallow depths from anticlines formed by drape over hogback ridges at the Wolfcampian unconformity formed by resistant beds on the flanks of the deep structures. Actually, every conceivable type of structural and stratigraphic trap is found on the Central Basin Platform and they are always filled with oil.

PB Figure 16 was selected from a series of east-west cross sections across the Central Basin Platform by D. G. Bebout and K. J. Meador (1985, please also see PB Figure 15). All cross sections on PB Figure 15 show high structural relief between the basins and the uplifted areas. They show a series of uplifted fault blocks and faulted anticlines in the lower half of each cross section and relatively unstructured platform deposits in the upper half.

Yates Field

Yates field is located at the southeast end of the Central Basin Platform (PB Figure 14C). All the stacked reservoirs of this field are Permian Guadalupian in age. They include all facies of the **platform-margin complex**. This same setting has yielded giant fields all around the edges of the Central Basin Platform (Permian Basin Figure 15) and is one of the reasons reservoirs in the **San Andres and Grayburg Formations have provided more than half of the total oil produced in the Permian Basin.**

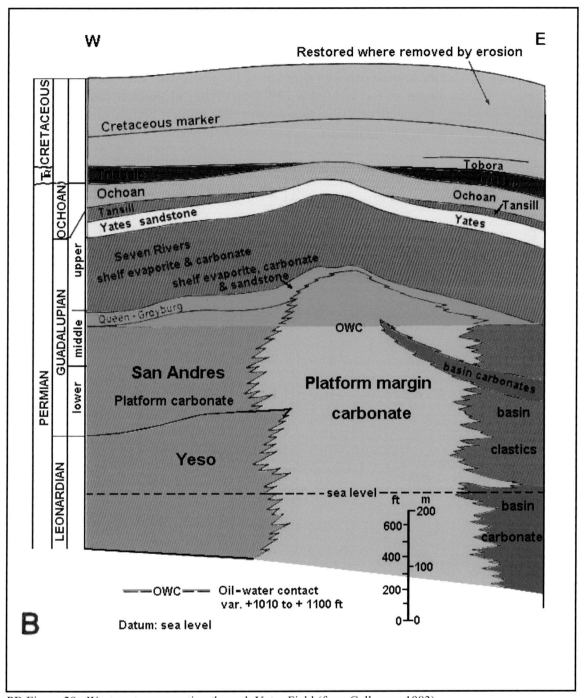

PB Figure 29. West-east cross section through Yates Field (from Gallaway, 1983).

The best reservoirs in Yates field are carbonates at the San Andres and Grayburg levels. Periodic widespread emergence during low sea level stands of the cyclothems allowed meteoric waters to dissolve parts of the limestone, leaving large cavities and caverns. The field also produces from sandstone reservoirs of sabkhas deposits in the overlying Queen and Seven Rivers Formations.

Oil had been discovered to the north in 1925 and 1926 in the McCamey and McElroy fields. The Yates field was discovered in 1926 by drilling on a surface anticline. The well blew out at a depth of 997 feet, was deepened to 1,032 feet, and was completed flowing 135 barrels of oil an hour. A subsequent development well was tested at the rate of 256,000 barrels per day. This may still be the highest capacity ever tested for an oil well anywhere in the world. The average drilling depth in the field is 1,250 feet. The oil column has a maximum thickness of 450 feet. Cumulative production is over 900 million barrels of oil. Ultimate production will be over one billion barrels.

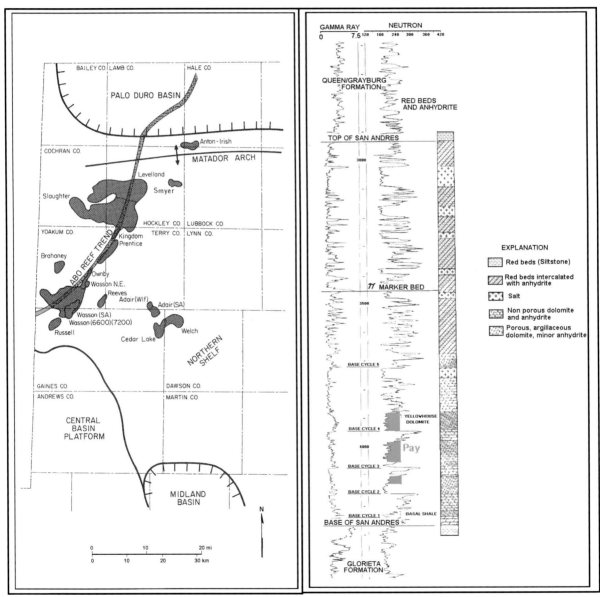

PB Figure 30. San Andres fields of the Northwest Shelf of the Midland Basin (from Gallaway, 1983).

PB Figure 31. Radioactive and sample log from the Levelland-Slaughter field (from Gallaway, 1983).

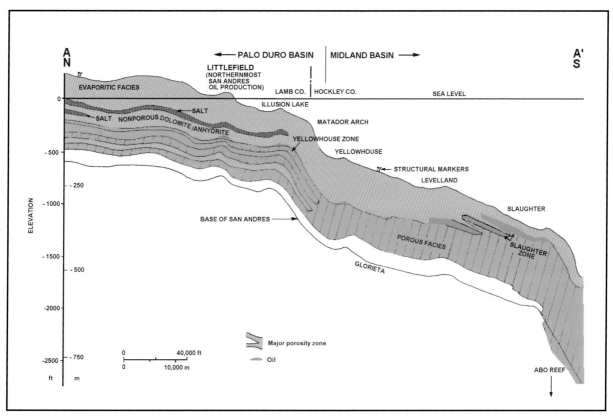

PB Figure 32. Northwest-southeast cross section showing lateral relations of Levellend-Slaughter pay intervals (after Gallaway, 1983).

Northwestern Shelf Permian Carbonate Fields

Carbonate reservoirs in the Leonardian Clearfork Formation and the lower part of the Guadalupian San Andres Formation in the Texas part of the Northwestern Shelf have a cumulative production of 3.2 billion barrels of oil from 16 fields. All the fields, except for Anton Irish, are located south of the Matador Arch in the northwest part of the Midland Basin. The same type of field is found in the continuation of the shelf across the northern end of the Delaware Basin in New Mexico. The shelf deposits originated as a series of cyclothemic southward progradations. With each successive cycle, the porous dolomite reservoirs developed a bit farther south in a shingle fashion. Additional subsidence in areas to the south caused the entire Northwestern Shelf area to be gently tilted to the south.

The dolomite reservoirs of both formations formed basinward of sabkha environments. The sabkhas, like those of the southern Persian Gulf today, were desert areas of evaporation where anhydrite, salt, and red siltstones were deposited. The evaporate facies formed an updip seal, and with progradation also formed a cap rock to individual reservoir sequences.

There are large accumulations in the mega-giant Watson and Levelland-Slaughter fields. The latter produces from simple stratigraphic traps formed by the updip limits of three cycles of deposition (Permian Basin Figures 30 to 32 from Gallaway, et al, 1983). Drilling depths are 4,900 to 5,000 feet. Cumulative production for Watson is over 1.4 and Levelland-Slaughter exceeds 1.2 billion barrels of oil.

Deep Water Sands of the Midland and Delaware Basins

During the Permian both basins were broad and fairly flat with a slight slope to the south. They were surrounded on three sides by wide carbonate shelves. The basins were relatively deep, probably averaging about 3,000 feet of relief between the shelves and the bottom of the basins. During the low stand parts of each cyclothem the carbonate shelves were exposed to erosion and river systems from mountains far to the east and north fed mud and sand though valleys to form submarine fans around the edge of the basin. During some cycles the mud and sand was deposited in broad very gentle fans that continued many miles down the length of the basin. PB Figure17 shows Spraberry sands in the Midland Basin. PB Figures 14C and 23 show the stratigraphic position of the deep-water sands in the Delaware Basin relative to the prograding reefs. The sands deposited far from the shelf edges were very fine-grained and usually fairly tight (they have poor permeability). They are interbedded with source beds and often filled with oil. Special technologies had to be developed to force cracks away from wells bores so that enough oil could be produced to provided a reasonable return on investment.

The Spraberry and Dean Deep Water Sandstones produce oil over a broad area of the Midland Basin at depths of 7,400 to 8,400 feet. Total production from hundreds of wells now exceeds 650 million barrels. In the New Mexico and Texas the Delaware and Cherry Canyon Sand production of the Delaware Basin is found in discreet channels at depths of 2,600 to 4,900 feet. Total production for the play is about 150 million barrels.

Since 2008 advances in technology including horizontal drilling and fracing have allowed the development of new major reserve plays, e.g. Barnett Shale of the Delaware Basin and Wolfcamp detrital sediments of the west side of the Midland Basin, that will add substantially to future recoverable oil and gas.

Chapter 5
Sierra Madera Astroblem
Pecos County, Texas

Sierra Madera (SM) Figure 1. Low angle view of part of the moon's surface. Red "C's" are alongside craters that have central peaks.

If you look at the moon through a telescope or good binoculars and find a region that has a low sun angle (lots of shadows), you will see that the surface is completely pockmarked with circular depressions of all sizes. Each depression was the result of a **meteorite or comet hitting the surface of the moon** with enough force to blast rocks outward and leave a crater, a so-called astroblem. Many of these craters have a **central conical peak** that looks like a volcano. **Seventeen miles south of Fort Stockton, US Highway 385 crosses** the western half of **a circular astroblem** that is **the best-exposed example of this type of crater in the United States**. It has a **600-foot high prominent central peak** called **Sierra Madera** (wooded hill) that is composed of intensely folded and faulted Permian limestone rocks that were originally more than 4,000 feet below ground. This central uplift is four miles in diameter. The depression around this central uplift is eight miles in diameter and the concentrically constructed outside rim is about one-half mile wide. The rocks of this rim are Lower Cretaceous carbonates that are locally folded and cut by concentric normal faults downthrown toward the center.

Detailed study of this astroblem began in 1960 by E. M. Shoemaker when travel to the moon was first contemplated. The main impetus was to obtain information on terrestrial examples of lunar structures. **Sierra Madera Astroblem** is so well preserved and exposed that it **should be either a state park or a national monument**.

The rocks of the central peak exhibit many features that record the severity of the impact. Brecciation (rock that is completely broken into angular pieces), shatter cones (high pressure impact structures in rocks), and certain types of internal structures of minerals at Sierra Madera are ascribed to shock deformation. The most common type of breccia consists of thoroughly shattered rocks in which the fragments are generally so little displaced that thin beds maintain their continuity. A second type of breccia contains fragments of different lithologies.

Shatter cones, a very common mode of rock failure in **cryptoexplosion (impact) structures,** are well developed in the Permian rocks of Sierra Madera. Within the area in which breccias and shatter cones occur, quartz grains commonly have cleavages and other planar elements characteristically formed by shock (Sierra Madera Figure 7). Wilshire, et al, (1972) concluded that shocked quartz in the mixed breccias indicates pressures of over 200 kilobars (kb) grading to 100 kb and 50 kb at the flanks of the uplift.

Holes drilled for oil and gas in formations below the astroblem, along with seismic data (that record reflections from formations deep in the earth), show that the intense deformation observed at the surface dies out rapidly below the surface and disappears between 6,000 and 8,000 feet. The gross structure is represented by a bowl-shaped body approximately 8.5 miles in diameter and 6,000 to 8,000 feet deep, the central part of which has a high structural relief near the present ground surface, with intensely shattered beds that are tightly folded and cut by numerous faults. The intensity of deformation and brecciation decreases outward and downward from the central peak.

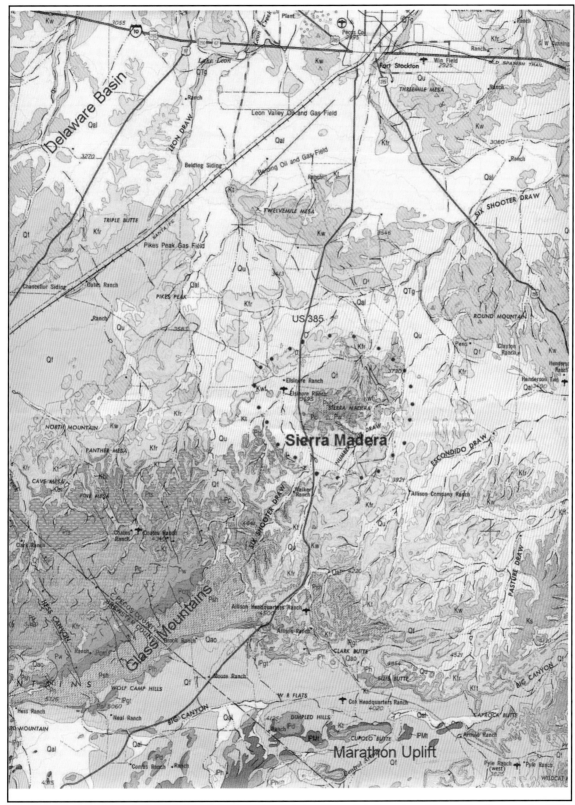

SM Figure 2. Geologic Map showing the location of the Sierra Madera Astroblem 17 miles south of Fort Stockton (from Geologic Atlas of Texas, Fort Stockton Sheet, 1994). Please see SM Figure 3 for an explanation of symbols.

SYSTEM	GROUP	FORMATION		REGIONAL		SIERRA MADERA	
				THICKNESS (FEET)	LITHOLOGY	THICKNESS (FEET)	LITHOLOGY
CRETACEOUS	Lower part of Washita Kw	Georgetown Limestone		200–740		30–475	
		Duck Creek Limestone					
	Fredericksburg Kwf	Kiamichi Formation				130–250	
		Edwards Limestone					
	Trinity	Basal Cretaceous sandstone	Kb	50–360		50–100+	
TRIASSIC		Bissett Conglomerate	Kb	0–500		0?	
PERMIAN		Tessey Limestone	Pt	400–1460		0–400	
		Gilliam Limestone	Pg	590–980		700–980	
		Word Formation Pw — Vidrio Limestone Member Pwv		280–1070		200–750	
		Sandstone member				0–35	
		Limestone member				0–250	
		Cathedral Mountain Formation	Pcm	0–1800		0–80	
		Hess Formation (King, 1930)	Ph Phv	1870–2850		1200–1400	
		Wolfcamp Formation (King, 1930)	Pwc	6995–12,220			
PENNSYLVANIAN	Strawn			0–850			
MISSISSIPPIAN		Barnett Shale equivalent	PMt PMd	70–450			
		Novaculite of Kinderhook(?) age	MDO	40–180			
DEVONIAN		Woodford Shale equivalent	MDO	70–255			
		Chert of Devonian(?) age	MDO	30–185			
SILURIAN		Fusselman Dolomite		15–190			
ORDOVICIAN		Montoya Dolomite		160–590			
	Simpson			2130–2480			
	Ellenburger			1420?			
CAMBRIAN				100?			
PRE-CAMBRIAN							

SM Figure 3. Generalized stratigraphic column of Paleozoic to Lower Cretaceous rocks at Sierra Madera (left column) and detailed stratigraphic column of rocks at Sierra Madera (right column, from Wilshire, et al, 1972).

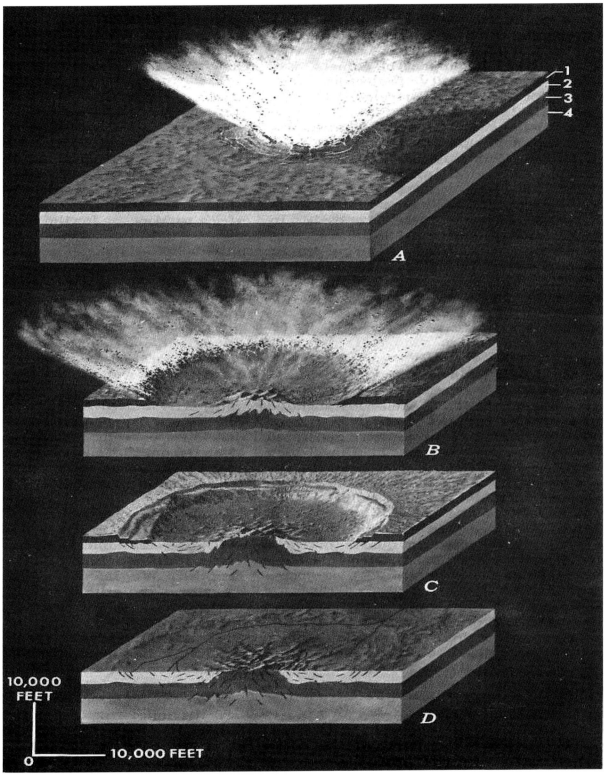

SM Figure 4.   From Wilshire, et al, 1972. Hypothetical reconstruction of events forming Sierra Madera. Layers of rock: 1. Post-Cretaceous (hypothetical); 2. Lower Cretaceous, and Permian Ochoan and Guadalupian strata; 3. Permian Leonard strata; and 4. Permian Wolfcamp strata. *A.* Shortly after impact showing growth of crater by low angle jetting. *B.* Seconds after *A*, showing crater growth by ejection and formation of overturned flap; *C.* Freshly formed crater days after impact, showing uplift protruding into crater, crater-rim modification by slumping, and fall-back, *D.* Present form of Sierra Madera, modified by erosion.

SM Figure 5. Aerial view of Central Peak from the northeast. Red arrows indicate the dip of some of the blocks in the uplifted and fractured Permian rocks of the peak. K identifies a syncline in Lower Cretaceous limestones. Airplane was provided by Betty Hargus and Bob Elliott was the pilot.

The ring depression separating the outer rim and the central uplift is largely buried under alluvium. Drill holes and outcrops on the southeast sideshow that the depression is floored by Cretaceous rocks that have dips up to vertical and are cut by faults. The depression is separated from the outer rim by concentric normal faults but is not separated from the central uplift by any significant change in style of deformation.

Compared with the setting and structure of surrounding Cretaceous strata and the nearby Pennsylvanian and Permian rocks of the Glass Mountains, the Sierra Madera is unique in its form, style, and severity of deformation. The Astroblem was formed sometime after the Lower Cretaceous strata were deposited. The next younger event recorded in the area is some mild Miocene or Pliocene faulting, but the nearest fault is too far removed from this area to provide any help in determining the age of impact. The best guess is that the feature formed during the Late Cretaceous or Early Tertiary.

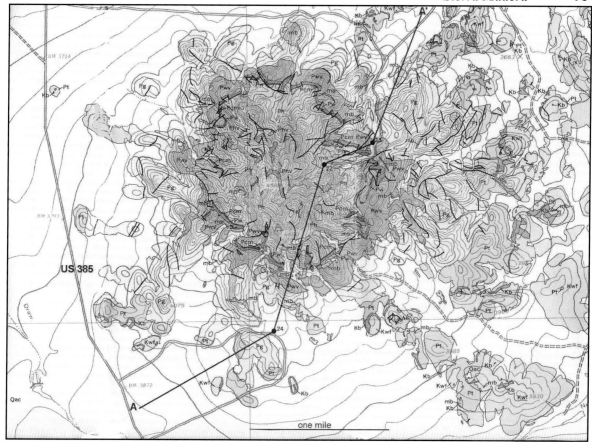

SM Figure 6. Geologic map of Central Peak. Please see Sierra Madera Figure 3 for an explanation of formation symbols (from Plate 2 of Wilshire, et al, 1972).

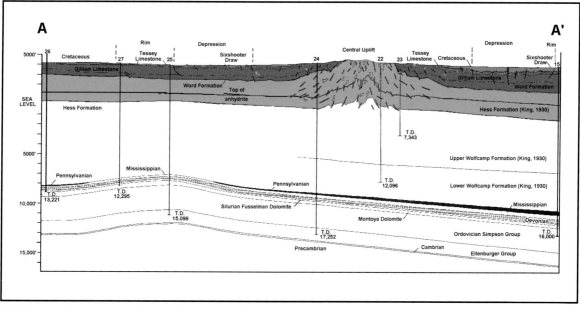

SM Figure 7. Cross section A-A' from southwest to northeast across the Central Peak. Line of section is posted on Figure 6. Please see Sierra Madera Figure 3 for an explanation of formation symbols (from Plate 2 of Wilshire, et al, 1972).

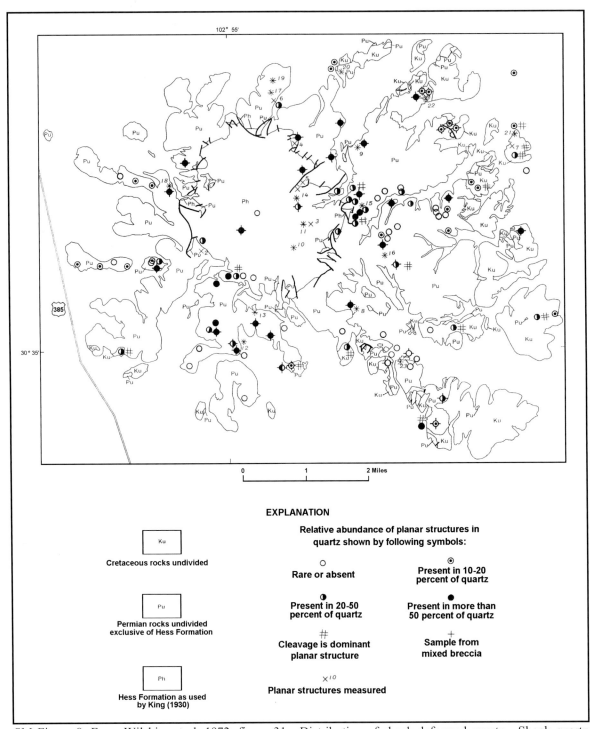

SM Figure 8. From Wilshire et al, 1972, figure 31. Distribution of shock-deformed quartz. Shock quartz provides one of the principle clues to the impact origin of the astroblem.

SM Figure 9. Aerial view of Central Peak looking southeast across west rim near gas plant. Fractured Cretaceous limestones of west rim in foreground; the alluvial covered ring depression in is middle ground. Airplane was provided by Betty Hargus and Bob Elliott was the pilot.

Astroblems have been found in many part of the world. They range in age from Precambrian for the Sudbury Complex of Ontario (Naldrett, 2003) and the Vredefort ring of South Africa, to the Miocene age Steinheim Basin of Germany. Present exposures show a wide range of erosional level. Astroblems have common characteristics that tie them together and allow the more deeply eroded structures, such as Sierra Madera, to be reconstructed by comparison with the astroblems that are less eroded. The structures at Flynn Creek, Tennessee and the Steinheim Basin represent the highest levels of exposure in well-studied astroblems. Both structures have a small central uplift surrounded and partly buried by a lens of breccia that occupies a shallow crater. A somewhat lower erosional level is preserved at Gosses Bluff, Australia, where some highly shocked and melted fallback breccia is preserved, but the original crater walls have been destroyed by erosion. Sierra Madera represents a still lower erosional level from which most vestiges of a crater-form depression, fallback, and ejecta have been stripped (Wilshire, 1972, p.37). Scaling to the dimensions of Flynn Creek crater and various experimental craters suggests that about 2,000 feet of cover may have been originally present over the Lower Cretaceous beds that has since been removed by erosion (Sierra Madera Figure 4).

Sierra Madera was extensively studied in preparation for lunar exploration. These results indicated that one could sample the thickness of lunar crust in the walls of craters and that rocks from the central uplifts would provide data on subcrater material from depths approximately one-tenth of the crater diameter. The typical lunar crater considered was over 15 miles in diameter. Thus sampling rocks from the central uplift would allow study of rocks from over 1.5 miles below the surface.

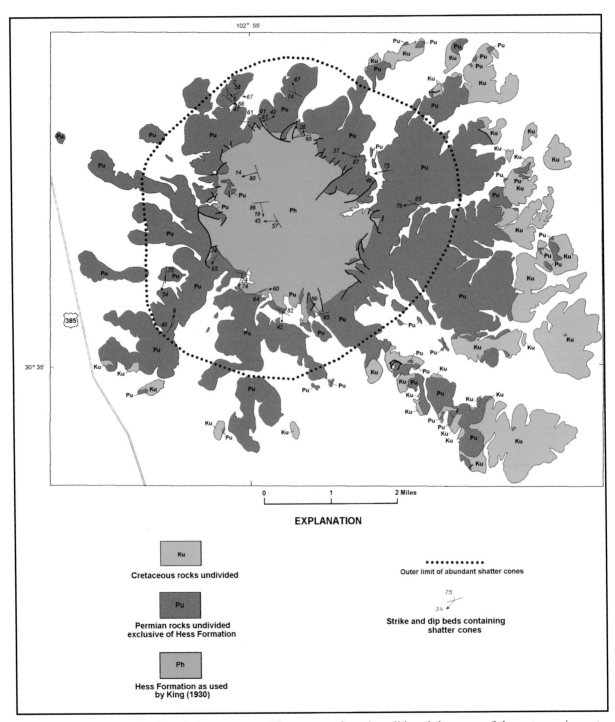

SM Figure 10. Distribution of shatter cones. These cones form in solid rock because of the extreme impact pressure (Wilshire, et al, 1972).

Chapter 6
Llano Estacado
The Southern High Plains of Texas

Llano Estacado (LE) Figure 1. Physiographic map of West Texas area showing the southern part of the High Plains, the Llano Estacado. M=Midland; A=Amarillo. Copyright 2001 by Ray Sterner, Johns Hopkins University Applied Physics Laboratory. Image reproduced courtesy of Ray Sterner.

The Llano Estacado is not as scenic as the other "Geologic Wonders" covered in this book, but like most geologic features, it becomes more interesting as one knows its history. The **Llano Estacado (Staked Plains)** is a high mesa (Llano Estacado (LE) Figure1) that slopes from west-northwest to east-southeast at a rate of approximately 10 feet per mile (from 4,500 feet above sea level northwest of Clovis, New Mexico to 2,500 feet near Big Springs, Texas). The Llano Estacado is the **southern part of the High Plains** (LE Figure 2), which extend from South Dakota to about 11 miles south of Midland, Texas. The High Plains are underlain by the Ogallala Formation. The Ogallala Formation, an important aquifer of the High Plains, is the erosional remnant of an extensive apron of stream and wind deposits that extended from the Rocky Mountains to far east of its present limit.

The total picture of the Llano Estacado is one of physical isolation. It is defined by the southern escarpment of the Canadian River valley on the north. Along the east side there is the irregular and deeply incised **Caprock escarpment**. The western boundary is the **Mescalero Escarpment** of New Mexico. The southern end of the plateau lacks a distinct boundary as it blends into the Edwards Plateau.

This chapter draws freely on work by various agencies, especially the Texas Bureau of Economic Geology, which has mapped the distribution of conglomerate and sandstone water reservoirs in the Ogallala aquifer. They have also modeled mathematically the hydrodynamics of the aquifer and projected future ground-water trends.

Generally the Llano Estacado is elevated 50 to 400 feet relative to the surrounding areas. It is semiarid with an average annual precipitation of 12 to 22 inches. Precipitation is higher in the east and lower at higher elevations in the west. There is a high rate of evaporation over the Llano Estacado, and the soils over this upland contain significant secondary accumulations of calcium carbonate. As a result, rainwaters soaking into the ground dissolve the calcium carbonate from the soils and sands, which in turn, because of the high rate of evaporation, is precipitated a meter or so below the ground surface as a hard layer of impervious limestone material commonly called **caliche** (calcrete of some).

The Ogallala Formation

The **Ogallala Formation** is of Miocene and Pliocene age (25 - 1.8 m.y.). The formation accumulated as a series of overlapping alluvial fans that headed in the Rocky Mountains. During Pleistocene and Recent times eolian (wind) processes smoothed the upper surface to provide the low relief we see now. Llano Estacado Figure 2 shows the present distribution of the Ogallala Formation. In southeastern Wyoming, there is a remnant of the original fan deposits that extends to the top of the Laramie Range. This area is known as the **"gangplank"** as the surface gradually rises to the top of the mountains. On the Union Pacific Railroad, which takes advantage of this gangplank, one can cross the mountains and not realize that you are crossing part of the Front Range. Elsewhere, the edges of the Ogallala are defined by post-Ogallala erosion.

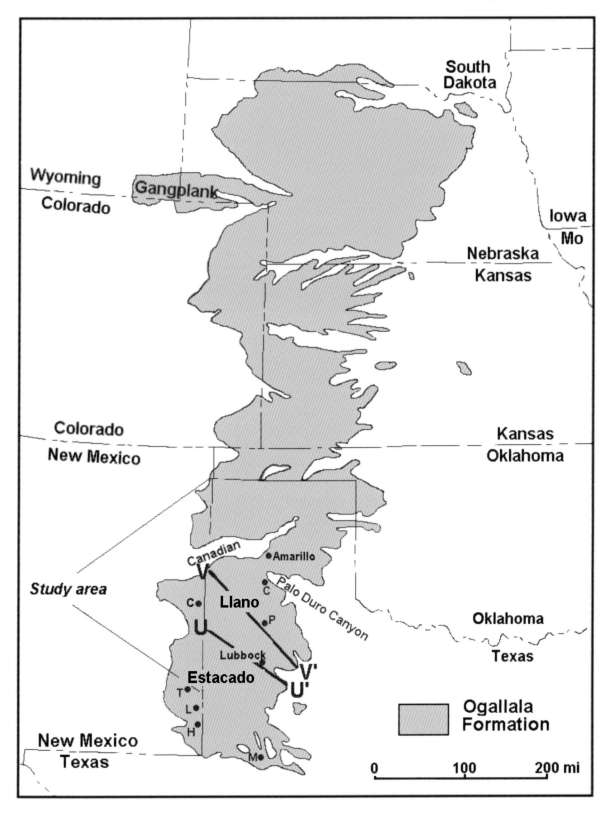

LE Figure 2. Index map showing extent of Ogallala Formation across the High Plains of Western United States. Map shows the preserved "gangplank" in southeast Wyoming (Nativ, 1988). Red lines V-V' and U-U' show the location of cross sections on LE Figures 9 and 10. C=Clovis (west) Canyon (East) P=Plainview T=Tatum L=Lovington H=Hobbs M=Midland.

LE Figure 3. View of part of west edge of Llano Estacado south of San Jon, New Mexico. The Cretaceous black shales exposed at the base of Dakota Sandstone at the sharp curve halfway down the escarpment on New Mexico Highway 469 contain remains of shallow water mollusks.

The Ogallala Formation is important to Texas and the nation as an aquifer that supplies much of the water used for High Plains agriculture. The areas of recharge for this aquifer are very limited. Recharge comes mainly from seepage from the numerous playa lakes found across the Llano Estacado (Mullican. et al, 1997). Withdrawals of water for irrigation far exceed natural recharge and have caused significant depletion of the Ogallala aquifer.

In addition to ground water, the Ogallala contains economically important aggregate resources (such as sand, gravel, and caliche) and may contain exploitable uranium deposits.

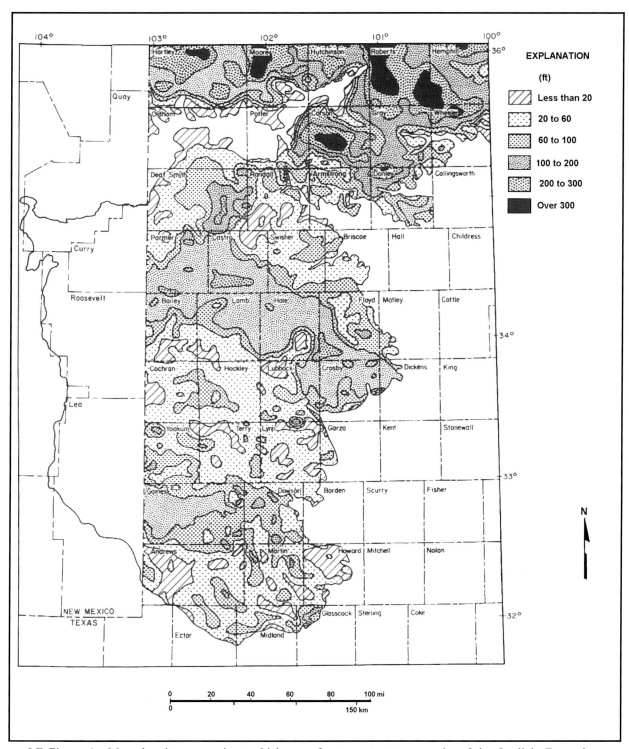

LE Figure 4.   Map showing approximate thickness of water-saturate reservoirs of the Ogallala Formation. Thickness of the aquifer reservoirs is highly controlled by the configuration of the sub-Ogallala surface (from Nativ, 1988).

In Chapter 6 on the Big Bend area, there is a discussion of the importance of the Miocene and Pliocene (Neogene) broad epierogenic uplift of the Southern Rocky Mountain area of the North American Continent in the development of rifts. The crest of the broad uplift of this part of the continent extended from Big Bend to central Wyoming and the width from the Mississippi River to the Sierra Nevada of California. The rifts are near the center of the uplift. They are tension cracks that resulted from the stretching caused by the broad warping of the crust. Prior to this uplift, the Southern Rockies had been reduced to an area of low relief hills and valleys that were filled by ash and debris from Oligocene volcanoes. The Miocene uplift rejuvenated the Rocky Mountains and accelerated the rate of erosion. The products of erosion, sand, conglomerate, and mud sediments were deposited as the Ogallala Formation in broad aprons across the High Plains area.

The distribution of the Ogallala sediments is illustrated in a series of figures:

LE Figure 5 shows the age of the rocks underlying different areas of this part of the High Plains. The Permian rocks contain thick sections of salt. Solution of this salt caused a broad solution zone northwest to southeast through the Amarillo area.

LE Figure 6 shows in four progressive panels how successive alluvial fans filled one low area and then spilled over to other low areas following the law of least resistance. A summary of Ogallala deposits over the Texas part of the High plains is shown on LE Figure 7.

The thickness map (LE Figure 8) of the Ogallala and Pleistocene deposits shows that drilling depths to the fresh water reservoir sections may be as much as 800 feet north of Amarillo and are generally less than 400 feet over the Llano Estacado.

LE Figures 9 and 10 are cross sections down the Clovis-Plainview (V-V') and Brownfield-Lubbock (U-U') fan lobes. These cross sections provide a good look at the hydrodynamics of downhill flow and the distribution of channel sands and conglomerates that contain the water.

A surficial blanket of Pleistocene deposits (<1.8 m.y.) over the Ogallala sediments has been named the Blackwater Formation (Gustavson, 1996). This formation consists of eolian sands and silts interbedded with numerous buried calcic (caliche) soils. Small ephemeral lakes are scattered over the Llano Estacado. One study (Mullican, et al, 1997) estimated that there are 19,250 playa lakes on the Southern High Plains. Most of the surface drainage of the Llano Estacado is into these lakes where the water, in turn, seeps into the aquifer. Studies in the Panhandle (Hovorka, 1995) identify up to six cycles of playa lake development in 55 feet of Blackwater section under some lakes.

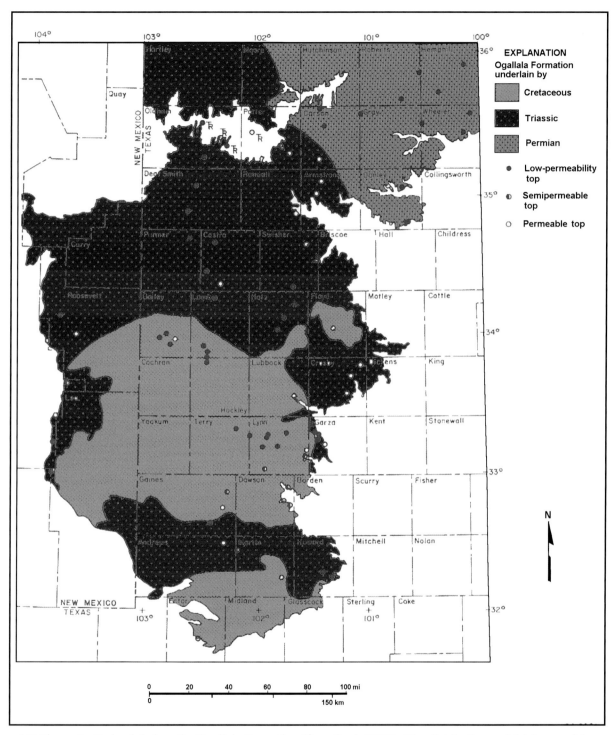

LE Figure 5. Bedrock below the Ogallala Formation (from Seni, 1980). The distribution and thickness of the Ogallala fans deposits was controlled by the manner in which the underlying rocks responded to erosion. Outliers of resistant strata, like the Cretaceous limestones, caused thin areas. The Ogallala is exceptionally thick where solution zones and collapse basins developed because of evaporites in Permian strata.

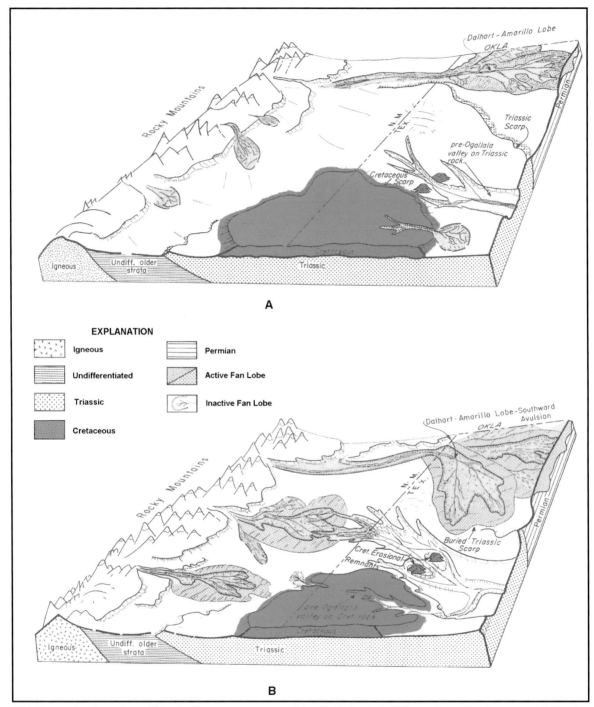

LE Figure 6. A series of block diagrams constructed by S. J. Seni (1980) to show development of the fan lobes east from the Rocky Mountains and relationships between fan lobes through time. **Block A**. Progradation of the Dalhart-Amarillo fan lobe. This fan lode occupies a topographic low formed by solution of Permian evaporites. **Block B**. Complete development of the Dalhart-Amarillo to the point of burial of the Triassic scarp and the beginning of progradation of the Clovis-Plainview fan lobe.

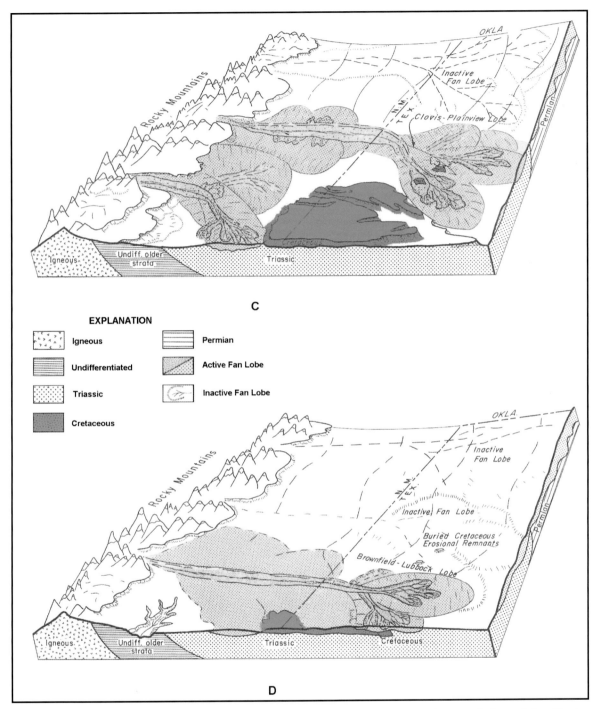

EXPLANATION

Igneous

Undifferentiated

Triassic

Cretaceous

Permian

Active Fan Lobe

Inactive Fan Lobe

LE Figure 6 (cont) Block C. Abandonment of Dalhart-Amarillo fan lobe and progradation of the Clovis-Plainview fan lobe into a major pre-Ogallala valley cut into Triassic strata. **Block D.** Late Ogallala abandonment of Clovis-Plainview fan lobe and progradation of Brownfield-Lubbock fan lobe across buried Cretaceous strata.

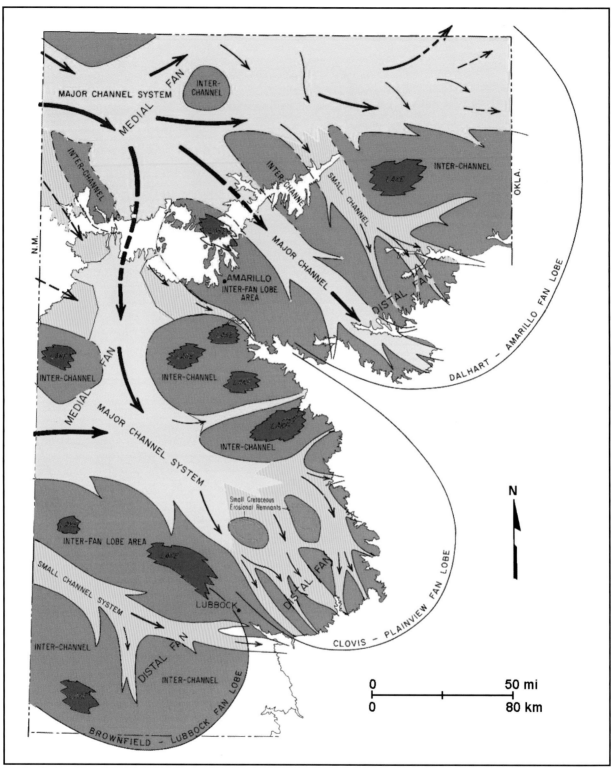

LE Figure 7. Distribution of fan deposits across Llano Estacado (from Seni, 1980).

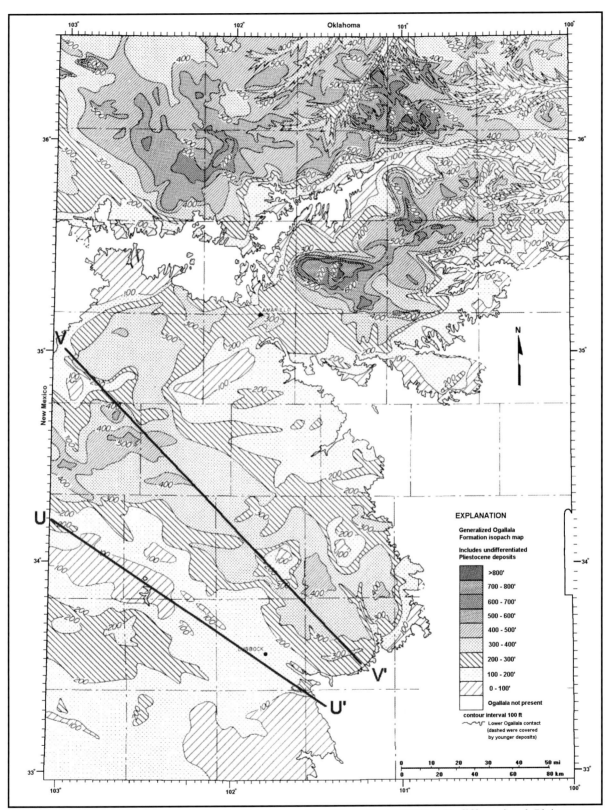

LE Figure 8. Thickness map of the Ogallala Formation (from Seni, 1980). Undifferentiated Pleistocene deposits up to 20 feet thick may be included in the totals. Red lines show the location of cross sections on LE Figures 9 and 10.

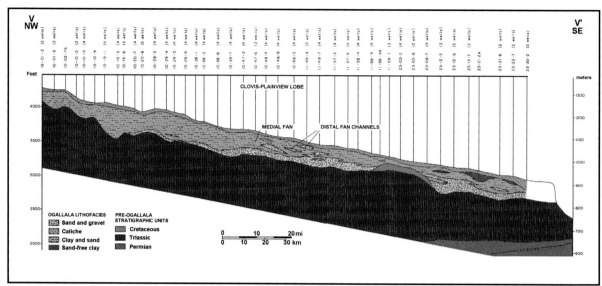

LE Figure 9. Dip section V-V' down axis of Clovis-Plainview fan lobe. The down dip increase in gravel percentage reflects steep valleys and high relief associated with Cretaceous erosional remnants that contributed locally derived gravels. Location of cross sections is on Figures 2 and 8.

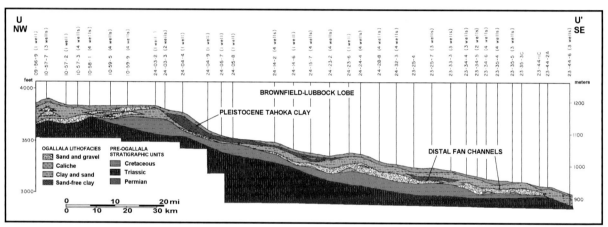

LE Figure 10. Dip section U-U' down axis of Brownfield-Lubbock fan lobe. Sand-free clay unit in the upper part of the Ogallala may be a Pleistocene deposit.

Solution of bedded salt is probably the main origin of the numerous playa lake depressions, especially near the edges of the Llano Estacado. Elsewhere solution, wind deflation, and animal activity have combined to enlarge small ponds to playa lakes. If one sees a bison taking a dust bath in a dry depression it is easy to mentally estimate the amount of dust generated by a few thousand bison that has been blown away by the West Texas wind. Given a few thousand years of this activity, small ponds will enlarge to miles-wide playas.

The tributaries of the Red, Brazos, and Colorado Rivers flowing east from the Llano Estacado have their origin on the caprock or from springs flowing from the down dip limit of Ogallala reservoirs. The amount of water flowing from the springs is unknown. The springs were all extremely important to early exploration and settlement of the High Plateau country.

Chapter 7
Volcanism across the Trans-Pecos Region of West Texas

The following three chapters cover specific areas of igneous intrusive and extrusive (volcanic) activities and mountain building in the Trans-Pecos (between the Rio Grande and Pecos Rivers) during middle Tertiary times (please see Inside Front Cover and Introduction Figure 1). The succession and timing of igneous events is measured by the radiometric dating of certain elements contained in the rocks.

Volcanism in the Trans-Pecos region of West Texas was limited to the period from 48 to 17 m.y. ago (late Eocene to Early Miocene times). During this time, volcanism was nearly continuous but varied considerably in location, style, composition, volume, and tectonic setting (Henry and McDowell, 1986).

The igneous intrusive and extrusive activity in Texas **is part of a much larger volcanic province** of generally similar age. The volcanic province extended westward into Mexico to include the very large **Sierra Madre Occidental province,** and northward through the Mogollon-Datil field of New Mexico to include the San Juan and Thirty-Nine Mile volcanic fields of Colorado (colored orange on Trans-Pecos Figure 1). Trans-Pecos Figure 1 is taken from the Tectonic Map of North America. In compiling this map, W. R. Muehlberger (1994) assigned the orange areas to the **"Durango Epoch"(43-25 m.y.),** which he described as a **distinctive period of very widespread igneous activity** during the middle part of the Tertiary Period.

The Sierra Madre Occidental igneous province of Mexico is believed the result of subduction of the Pacific Plate under that part of the continent during the Durango Epoch. The reason for the Trans-Pecos to San Juan igneous events, far from the edge of the continent, is not known.

The earliest igneous activity of the Trans-Pecos Region occurred in the form of widespread, locally abundant, small, mafic to acidic intrusions and basalt lavas in the Big Bend region. **The time interval 37-35 m.y. ago was an active time for the Trans-Pecos region, especially in the Davis Mountains.** Numerous extrusive centers and intrusions occurred over the Trans-Pecos region. **About 35 m.y. ago igneous activity shifted markedly from the central to the southern part of the Trans-Pecos region.**

There was a fundamental change in tectonic setting for this part of the North American continent about 31 m.y. ago. After that time, volcanic activity was very limited. Two overlapping volcanic centers formed in adjacent Chihuahua about 30 and 28 m.y. ago (T-P Figure 8). Shortly after the Chihuahua events and nearby in Texas, the Bofecillos volcano, which was an alkalic, mafic to intermediate, stratovolcano erupted.

Trans-Pecos (T-P) Figure 1. Map is southwestern part of the Tectonic Map of North America. Major mid-Tertiary igneous provinces are colored orange and identified (from Muehlberger, 1992).

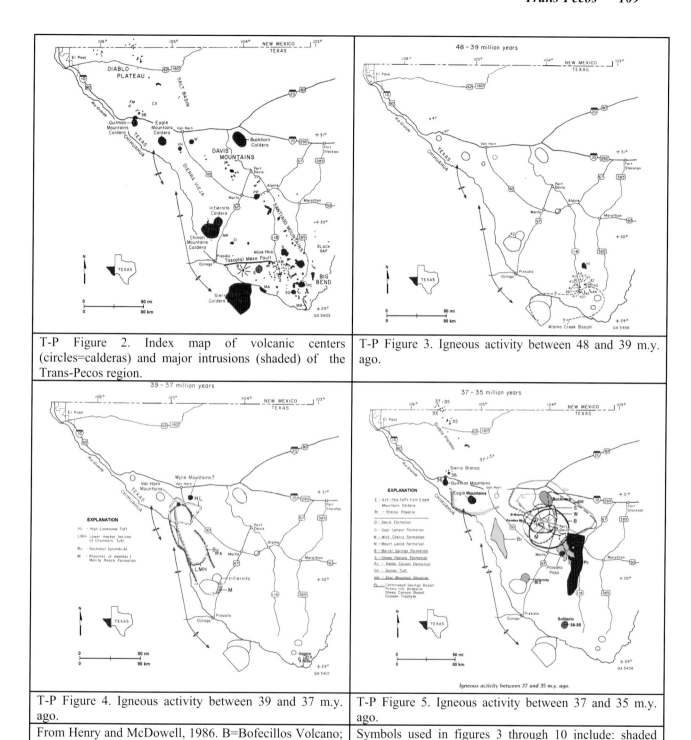

T-P Figure 2. Index map of volcanic centers (circles=calderas) and major intrusions (shaded) of the Trans-Pecos region.

T-P Figure 3. Igneous activity between 48 and 39 m.y. ago.

T-P Figure 4. Igneous activity between 39 and 37 m.y. ago.

T-P Figure 5. Igneous activity between 37 and 35 m.y. ago.

From Henry and McDowell, 1986. B=Bofecillos Volcano; CI=Cienaga Mountains; CX=Cox Mountain; FM=Findley Mountains; MA=Mesa de Anguila; MM=Mariscal Mountain; MR=Morita Ranch; PC=Pine Canyon caldera; PP=Paisano Pass caldera; S=Solitario; SB=Sierra Blanca; SQ= Sierra Quemada caldera; VH= Van Horn Mountains caldera; W= possible Wylie Mountains caldera; XM= Christmas Mountains; 9= Nine Point Mesa.

Symbols used in figures 3 through 10 include: shaded area=intrusion emplaces during this time interval; colored outlined areas= original distribution of volcanic units erupted during this interval; "?"= indicates approximate outline where extent is extremely uncertain; crosshatched area=caldera active during this interval; solid lines=major dikes emplaced during this interval.

T-P Figures 3 to 9 are from Henry and McDowell, 1986 with changes in the age assignments of some units after personal communication with C. D. Henry, 2004.

The last volcanic activity in Texas occurred between 24 and 17 m.y. ago during the development of rift structures across the Trans-Pecos region. This activity consisted of widespread, but volumetrically minor, intrusions of basalt as dikes, lava flows, small stocks, and rarely as sills. Any extrusive material associated with these features has long since been removed by erosion.

The next three chapters will discuss the geology of major volcanic centers of the Davis Mountains, Big Bend region, and the Solitario-Bofecillos area. The other volcanic areas of Trans-Pecos, from the Chinati Mountains to the several centers near Van Horn, are covered individually in papers in the Bureau of Economic Geology Guidebooks 19 (Walton and Henry, 1979) and 23 (Price et al., 1986).

Igneous Rocks

In the Introduction (Chapter I), recommend that the layman reader leaf through freshman physical and historical geology textbooks and read the captions under the pictures. Review of this type will answer a lot of questions about all rock types, but will be especially useful in illustrating the various types and varieties of igneous rocks and structures. Igneous rocks can be very confusing as to the terminology applied to different rock types. Further, igneous terminology has been changed repeatedly as more research has been added so that non-igneous experts, like the author, are also often confused.

Igneous rocks originate in magma melts deep in the earth. Magmas of the Trans-Pecos region all appear to have originated in the mantle and to have started with a mafic or basic chemistry. Once formed the hot liquid melts were lighter than the surrounding rocks and rose towards the surface. As they rose they melted and assimilated the rock that was penetrated. The assimilation of new material progressively changed the chemical makeup of the magmas from basic (mafic) to acidic (felsic silicic). In the lava flows from Trans-Pecos volcanoes it is not unusual for a basic flow (basalt) to be interbedded with acidic rhyolite or trachyte flows as different parts of the magma chamber contribute to the extrusions.

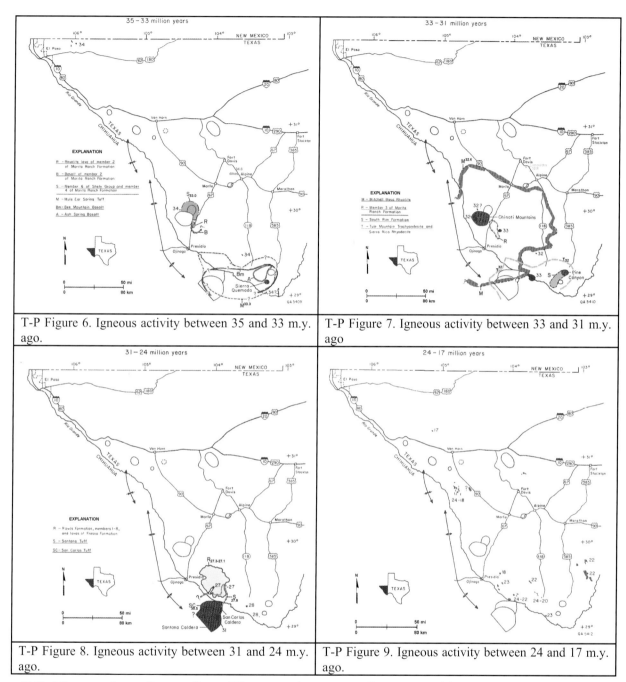

T-P Figure 6. Igneous activity between 35 and 33 m.y. ago.

T-P Figure 7. Igneous activity between 33 and 31 m.y. ago

T-P Figure 8. Igneous activity between 31 and 24 m.y. ago.

T-P Figure 9. Igneous activity between 24 and 17 m.y. ago.

T-P Figures 6 to 9 are from Henry and McDowell, 1986 with changes in the age assignments of some units after personal communication with C. D. Henry, 2004.

T-P Table 1:

Igneous Rocks	Acidic	Intermediate	Basic
	Cooler magmas		Hotter magmas
	Felsic silicic		Mafic
	Increasing iron and magnesium$\Rightarrow$		
	Decreasing silica$\Rightarrow$		
Extrusive and fine-grained intrusive rocks			
	rhyolite trachyte dacite	**andesite**	**basalt**
Intrusive - course grained rocks			
	granite/granodiorite syenite	**diorite**	**gabbro anorthosite**

An adjective that is used in describing many fine-grained igneous rocks is "porphyry' or 'porphyritic". This adjective is applied to rocks that have crystals in a matrix that is finer than the crystals. In the Davis Mountains, trachyte porphyries are common. The crystals are usually anorthoclase feldspar that is 0.5 mm or less in diameter and look like small snow flakes floating in a very fine-grained matrix. The anorthoclase is clear and the matrix may vary from gray to red-brown.

As magma rises it will intrude overlying rocks as shown in Trans-Pecos Figure 10. In the Trans-Pecos region we will see every type of intrusive feature shown.

Extrusive igneous rocks are deposited when the magma breaks through to the surface. The type of feature formed at the surface depends on the temperature and chemistry of the magma. Basic magmas are hotter (around 2,000 degrees centigrade) and have less gas. The extrusive rocks from them include explosive ash and pieces of lava that build small cinder cones, and extrusions of liquid lava that often results in long (sometimes many miles) basalt lava flows. Volcanoes developed by basic extrusives are usually the low relief shield type. Hawaiian volcanoes are examples of shield volcanoes.

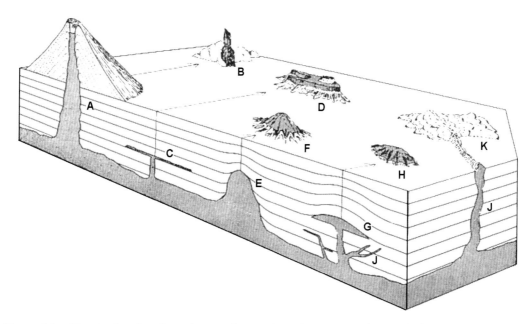

T-P Figure 10. Sketch showing intrusions and extrusions in cross section and plan view (from Maxwell, 1979). A Volcanic neck (sometimes called pipe or stock), the feeder pipe for a volcano. B, Volcanic neck after erosion has removed the cone. C. Sill, sheet of igneous rock that has spread laterally between layers of rock. D, A sill exposed by erosion. E, Intrusive plug that forced its way upward through bedded rocks. F, The top of a plug uncovered by erosion with upturned beds exposed on the flanks. G, Laccolith, a sill that widened upwards to form a lens-shaped body. Laccoliths have flat bases and arch the overlying rocks. H, Eroded laccolith exposed at the surface. J, Dike, intrusive rock that fills a fissure that cuts across bedded rocks. A dike usually is a nearly vertical wall-like body. K, Lava flow that came from a dike feeder, common source for lava flows in the Trans-Pecos.

Acidic and intermediate magmas are cooler (700 to 1,500 degrees centigrade) and are usually explosive. As with Mount St. Helens, they can blow out with tremendous force and spread debris over large areas. In some cases the ash cloud is incandescent hot and incinerates everything covered. Such clouds are called *nuee ardente*. As the ash settles a hard rock is formed as the hot particles fuse together. The resulting rock type is a welded tuff (ignimbrite).

Lava flows from acidic volcanoes usually are viscous and not widespread. The lava flows from intermediate and acidic volcanoes of the Trans-Pecos region were hotter than normal and often extended a long distance from the source.

The St. Helens type conical volcano results from a series of eruptions of ash and volcanic bombs (pieces of lava). When this type of volcano gets large, rains will cause the ash to become mud and very destructive mudflows (lahars) result. A sudden mudflow in Columbia in 1985 buried 22,000 people.

Radiometric dates

 It is probable that there will be occasions in the next three chapters where more than one date will be stated for the same igneous rock.   In compiling the data for the Trans-Pecos Region, I researched radioactive date data published over the last 50 years.   During that time, the type of raw material used for dating and the techniques used and the accuracy of the technology have been steadily evolving.   It is not unusual for the dates calculated for the same rock to have changed over a million years as new work is done.   Please be charitable if you find a situation where rocks with an older date happen to overlie rocks with a younger date.

T-P Figure 11. Davis Mountains. Scenic Loop Road. View northwest from State Highway 166 at the eroded end of a dike.

Chapter 8
Davis Mountains
Pecos, Brewster, Jeff Davis, Reeves
and Presidio Counties, Texas

The Davis Mountains are the eroded remnant of a volcanic field that had many volcanic centers. This **composite pile of volcanic rocks** is estimated to have covered five times the present aerial extent of approximately 2,000 square miles. The Davis Mountains lie over the southeast end of the Diablo Platform (please see the Permian Basin Chapter). The Davis Mountains, like the Diablo Platform, are bounded on the northeast by the Delaware Basin and on the southwest by the Marfa Basin. Elevations in the Davis Mountains range from 4,800 feet to peaks of 6,809 feet, such as Mount Locke, site of the McDonald Observatory, and 8,381 feet at Mount Livermore.

The Davis Mountains were formed during the Late Eocene. The were **six pulses of volcanic activity at approximately 300,000 year intervals in the 1.5 million year period between 36.8 and 35.3 m.y. ago** (Henry and others, 1994). Later, two groups of felsic salicic intrusions were emplaced at 34.6 and 32.8 m.y. The igneous extrusive rocks of this volcanic pile predate any of the volcanic activity in the Big Bend National Park or Big Bend Ranch State Park areas (Henry and McDowell, 1986). The Davis Mountain volcanic activity was contemporaneous with that in the Quitman, Eagle, and Infiernito Mountains (please see Trans-Pecos Figure 5).

The extrusive units of the Davis Mountains are unusual in several respects. To the layman they look like typical volcanic outpourings with many ash beds and lava flows that have typical weathering along vertical columnar joints. To the geologist they are somewhat weird. The extrusives are intermediate to acidic rocks (trachytes, quartz trachytes and rhyolites). They are usually porphyritic with snow-flake like crystals of feldspar. One weird fact is that the crystals in the porphyries are often anorthoclase, which is chemically a very basic crystal, in an acidic matrix. This indicates a very deep origin for the parent magma and a complex history of mixing deep and shallow melts as the magma rose to the surface.

Another illustration of the uniqueness of Davis Mountain lavas is the continuing discussion by experts of the nature of the lava flows. All agree they were surprising fluid and covered large areas. Some workers have proposed welded tuff (ignimbrite) origins; others say they are pure lavas; and there is even a third school that has them somewhere in between. In this chapter we will label them "lava flows".

There are many widespread, sheet-like deposits. Most appear to spread laterally from vents or broad shield volcanoes (volcanic centers) rather than from volcanic cones. An example of a fissure vent can be seen in the current site of eruption on Kilauea Volcano in the Hawaiian Islands. The eruption is coming up a fault far down the southeast side of the volcano. Periodically lava will pour out of other places along the 20-mile long fault.

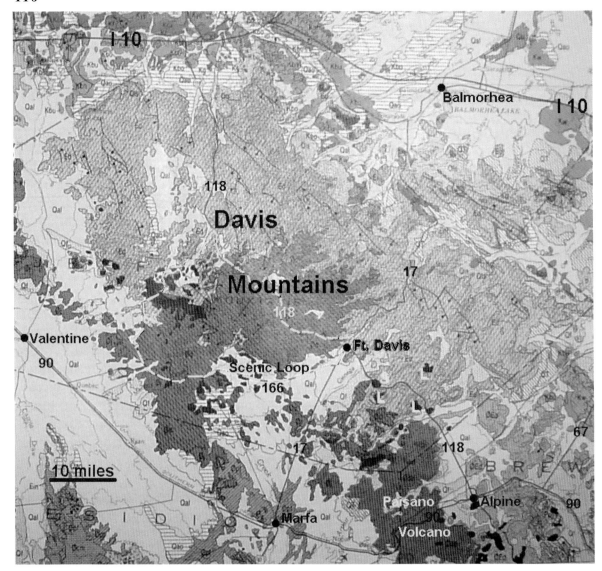

Davis Mountains (DM) Figure 1. Geologic Map of Davis Mountains (Bureau of Economic Geology Geologic Atlas Marfa and Fort Stockton Sheets). Scale is west of Marfa. L=laccolith; S=stock. Formation symbols are listed on Marfa and Fort Stockton Sheets.

One gets the impression that the magmas of the Davis Mountains were considerably hotter that those normally associated with quartz-rich rocks. Acidic volcanoes usually come from gassy magmas with fairly low temperatures (700-1,100 degrees centigrade). Like Mounts St. Helens and Rainier, acidic magmas usually feed high volcanic cones. Deposits from gassy volcanoes include lava flows, mud flow deposits, welded tuffs (ignimbrites) and bedded tuff (air-fall volcanic ash) units.

Except locally, there are surprising few widespread mudflow (lahar) deposits in the Davis Mountains. We will discuss this type of deposit in the caldera of Paisano volcano and along the Ridge Road in Davis Mountain State Park, but these exposures are the exception, not the rule. In volcanic areas that have intermediate to acidic chemistry mudflow deposits are usually abundant and make up a high percentage of the extrusive deposits. The volcanoes of those areas usually have high relief, a conical shape, are gassy (explosive), and erupt abundant volcanic bombs and ash that accumulate around the cone and then flow down hill at high speeds after each heavy rain.

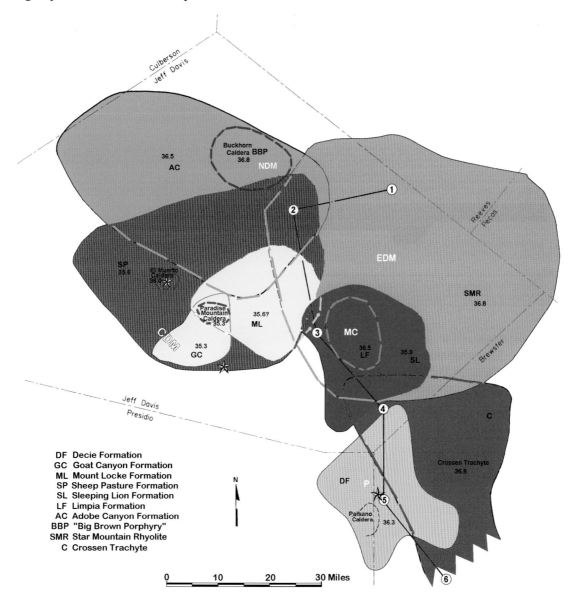

DF Decie Formation
GC Goat Canyon Formation
ML Mount Locke Formation
SP Sheep Pasture Formation
SL Sleeping Lion Formation
LF Limpia Formation
AC Adobe Canyon Formation
BBP "Big Brown Porphyry"
SMR Star Mountain Rhyolite
C Crossen Trachyte

DM Figure 2. Distribution of major lava units and eruptive centers, Davis Mountains area (after Henry and McDowell, 1986). Volcanic centers: P= Paisano, CDM= central Davis Mountains; MC= Musquiz; NDM= northeastern Davis Mountains; EDM= eastern Davis Mountains. Bold lines connect areas used in construction of correlation diagram of DM Figure 3. Stars indicate major intrusive centers.

Alpine Area

The boulders used in the landscaping of Sul Ross University are from the bedrock of the Alpine town site, which is the Crossen Trachyte. There are exposures of this bedrock in road cuts along US Highway 90 just east of town. The Crossen Trachyte and the underlying Pruett Tuff came from the Musquiz volcanic center southeast of Fort Davis (DM Figures 2 and 3).

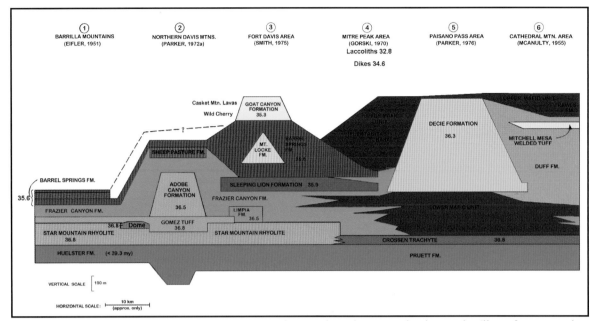

DM Figure 3. Diagram showing relative extents and ages of Davis Mountains lava units (line of cross section shown in DM Figure 2, after Henry and McDowell, 1986, modified with dates from Henry and others, 1994).

Traveling west from Alpine US Highway 90 crosses the southern part of the Paisano Volcano. This volcano was over 10 miles in diameter and developed in two stages. The prominent Twin Peaks west of Alpine are on the southeast flank of the Paisano volcano. D. F. Parker, 1979, pictures this volcano like the rest of the centers in the Davis Mountains, as being a relatively low relief shield volcano. The extrusive section from the volcano includes:

Upper Mafic Unit. (a few meters thick, largely removed by erosion)

Decie Formation

Upper Shield-Forming Unit. Quartz trachyte, trachyte and minor rhyolites, 400+meters thick in Paisano Peak area.

There appears to be periods of explosive activity during both the Lower and early Upper unit deposition when the volcano built a sizable cone and thick mud-flow (lahar) sections were deposited. These periods may have preceded the caldera collapse, as they are included in the profoundly disrupted terrains. Upper lavas of the Upper Unit are not involved, dating the collapse as during the early part of the Upper Unit deposition.

Lower Shield-forming Unit. (Several small ash-flow sheets at the base, porphyritic quartz trachytic tuff and lava, 340+ meters thick in main outcrop area near Mitre Peak)

Rhyolite Unit. Includes both intrusive domes and plugs and lava flows. The lava flows were viscous and only flowed 2 miles (3 KM) at most. Distinctive peralkaline rhyolites called **paisanite** occur in this unit and are characteristic of it.

Lower Mafic Unit. Crops out only in the Mitre Peak area where there are basalt flows, a few trachyte flows and interbedded sedimentary rocks. Unit is 1178 feet (360 meters) thick six miles north of Alpine.

DM Figure 4. Satellite image of southeast part of Davis Mountains. Reproduced with permission of Tobin International Ltd.

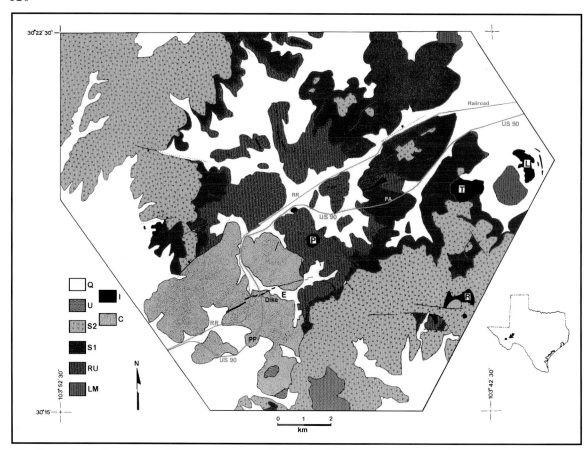

DM Figure 5. Geologic map of Paisano area (Don F. Parker, 1983). LM= Lower Mafic Unit. Decie Formation members: RU= Rhyolite unit; S1= Lower Shield unit; S2= Upper Shield unit; U= Upper Mafic unit; C= caldera collapse terrane. I= intrustion. Q=alluvium and coluvium. Heavy lines are faults with bars on downthrown side, dotted where concealed. Thin lines are dikes. Geographic localities: P= Paisano Peak; T= Twin Sisters; L= Lizard Mountain, R= Ranger Peak; E= Paisano Baptist encampment; PA= Picnic area; PP= Paisano Pass; RR=railroad.

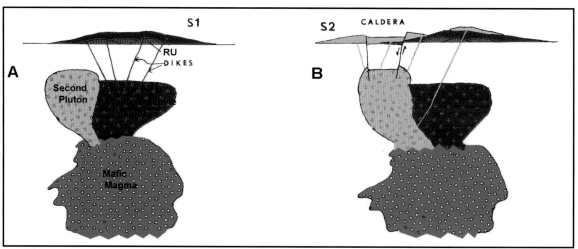

DM Figure 6. Conceptual diagram by Don F. Parker (1983, fig.1) illustrating possible magmatic evolution of the Paisano volcano. A: Upward movement of mafic magma melts rocks in the crust to add lighter acidic materials to the magma, which differentiates and extrudes rhyolites and/or trachyte some of the time and basalt at other times. This diagram shows the extrusion of the early rhyolite unit (RU on DM Figure 5), and S1, the Lower Shield unit. B: Shows extrusion of S2, the Upper Shield unit from a separate magma and the caldera that resulted from collapse after the eruption.

US Highway 90 Road log west across Paisano Volcano from Alpine to Paisano Pass

0.0   Intersection US Highway 90 and northbound State Highway 118 in center of Alpine.

1.9   Railroad overpass.

2.7   At 11:00 the peaks called Twin Sisters are syenite intrusions. At 12:00 the Decie Formation is composed of rhyolite and trachyte porphyries, tuff, and tuffaceous sediments, and some basalt from the Paisano volcanic center. At 3:00, on skyline, the Decie Formation overlies the Lower Mafic basalt. Looking north note the low angle east slopes of the Paisano Volcano that is characteristic of shield volcanoes.

4.6   Entering the southern part of first stage of the growth of this volcano.

5.7   Picnic Area on right. South of and subparallel to the highway are an east-west trending swarm of quartz trachyte dikes that radiate from the center of the first stage volcano. Straight-ahead is **Paisano Peak**, which is the syenite neck (feeder pipe) of a volcano that postdates the formation of the lower part of the shield volcano. This neck and the Twin Sisters intrusives were probably emplaced at the same time.

10.1   Road cut on south side of highway. This is an excellent exhibit of collapsed and brecciated blocks of the collapse caldera of the upper part of the shield volcano. The cut is near the northeast edge of the caldera. There is a jumble of different rock types. Hydrothermal (rising hot water) alteration of ash and part of the rocks has created thick white clay zones between blocks.

10.9   Turnoff to Baptist Camp.

11.0   At the middle of the curve there is a road cut through **a dike. Please be careful of fast traffic.** This vertical wall of solid, finely crystalline, **intrusive rock** is very different than the extrusive rocks in road cuts of this area. This is the longest dike in the Paisano Volcano.

11.5   Southside road cuts exposed mudflow (lahar) deposits in the caldera.

12.5   Road cuts expose mudflow deposits.

12.6   Paisano Pass. This point is near the center of the caldera. Elevation of 5,116 feet is the highest point on US Highway 90 between both coasts. Legend recounts that two Spaniards meeting here greeted each other as "Mi Paisano" (my countryman). First historical record is by Juan Dominquez de Mendoza, who camped here January 3, 1684. After 1850, the pass was a well-known point of the Chihuahua Trail, an immigrant route to California. Road cuts show west dip of this flank on the volcano.

13.4   Historical Marker. Now entering Marfa Basin and leaving the Davis Mountains.

End of road log.

DM Figure 7. US Highway 90 MP 10.1. Mudflow deposits in road cut near northeast edge of caldera. Observer is Katherine McGookey.

DM Figure 8. US Highway 90 MP 10. Hydrothermal alteration along contact between collapse blocks.

DM Figure 9. US Highway 90 MP 10.1. Broken blocks of porphyritic lava in collapse area near northeast edge of caldera.

DM Figure 10. US Highway 90 MP 11.0. Road cut on west side of highway. Andesite dike is intruded into mudflow deposits.

DM Figure 11. View southwest from State Highway 118 MP 8.9. Mitre Peak and the dike are intrusives dated at 34.6 m.y. Thus, they post-date all of the extrusive rocks of this area, but pre-date the cores of the laccoliths.

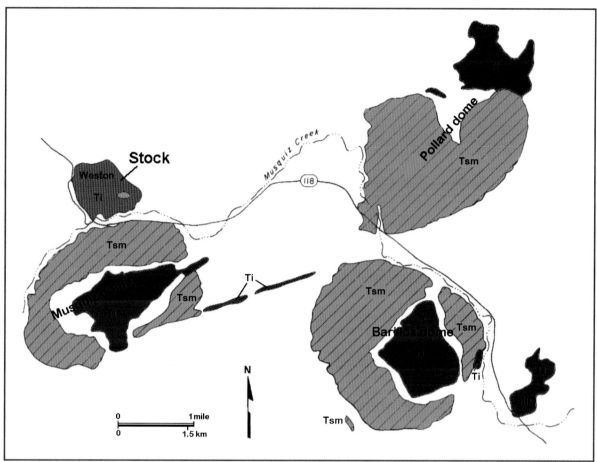

DM Figure 12. State Highway 118 road log. There are three laccoliths and the Weston Stock between Alpine and Fort Davis (Parker, et al, 1986, fig. 53, p.71).

DM Figure 13. State Highway 118 M P 8.9. Looking northwest into 32.8 m.y. old core of Barillos Laccolith. Please note broad arching around core. The intrusive rocks that core the laccoliths on DM Figure 12 are the youngest igneous rocks in the Davis Mountains.

Texas 118 Road log from Alpine to Fort Davis

Mileage

0.0   Junction US Highway 90 and State Highway 118.

2.6   Excellent examples of **coalescing alluvial fans** at the base of the hills west of the highway. The hills are Decie Formation quartz trachyte lava flows that form the distal part of the lava shield of the Paisano Volcano.

8.9   Top of rise, suggest a **Stop** across from corrals. Cliff-forming unit to north is a **Sleeping Lion Formation lava flow** from the **Musquiz volcanic center** east of Fort Davis. Straight ahead is the circular **Barillos laccolith**. This intrusive dome is younger than the Sleeping Lion flow, which can be seen again uplifted on the skyline northwest of the dome. Within the dome older Star Mountain Formation, lavas are breached to expose part of the intrusive core.

To the west is **Mitre Peak, which is a volcanic neck** of rhyolite. The neck intrudes Decie Formation extrusives from the Paisano Volcano. Northeast of Mitre Peak, trending towards the highway, is a **dike** that was probably fed by magma coming up the neck.

9.1   FM Road 1837 to Mitre Peak camp.

9.7   A quartz trachyte sill intrudes basalts of the Frazier Canyon Formation in this road cut.

11.1   Road enters Musquiz Canyon around the northeast side of the Barillos Laccolith. On the right, bedded tuff and basalt lava of the Frazier Canyon Formation underlie lava of the Sleeping Lion Formation.

13.0   Road is at the top of the Star Mountain lavas along southwest side of **Pollard Laccolith**. The Star Mountain Formation has been domed by a largely unexposed intrusion.

16.0-   Road cuts are in Limpia Formation trachyte, which is overlain by bedded tuff of the
17.1   Frazier Canyon Formation.

17.2   Picnic area. The Musquiz laccolith is to the left. Star Mountain Formation lavas are domed by the intrusion.

17.9   Historical Marker: "Musquiz Ranch – Ruins of the ranch home of Samuel Musquiz, a pioneer who settled here in 1854. Abandoned due to Indian raids. The deserted buildings served as a Ranger station intermittently, between 1880 - 1882, while the country was being cleared of Indians and bandits."

DM Figure 14. Looking south from Skyline Scenic Drive in Davis Mountains State Park. Hospital Canyon in foreground (the Fort is to the left at the mouth of the canyon), hoodoos eroded in top of Sleeping Lion Lava in middle ground, and part of the town of Fort Davis and Mitre Peak are in distance.

128

DM Figure 15. Rounded boulders of frothy obsidian in a mudflow exposed in long road cut along Skyline Scenic Drive of Davis Mountains State Park.

18.1   Part of the southwest flank of the **Weston Stock** (DM Figure 12) is exposed in the small valley at 3:00.

19.1   Road bed is in the Weston Stock intrusive rocks. Road follows the contact of the intrusion with older volcanic strata

19.2   Highway crosses a fault (east side is up) between the Weston intrusion and the Sleeping Lion Formation.

19.4   Turn off to Chihuahua Desert Research Center's visitor facility. At 1:00, the McDonald Observatory can be seen on Mount Locke.

20.3   The Sleeping Lion Formation is exposed on either side of the highway.

22,8   Dolores Mountain at 9:00 is capped by a Barrel Springs ash-flow sheet. The quarry at the tip of the mesa was the source of some of the pink stone mentioned below.

23.0   Fort Davis town center. Turn right on State Highway 17. The Limpia Hotel and Fort Davis Bank were constructed partially with pink welded ash-flow tuff quarried from the base of the Barrel Springs Formation.

24.0   Fort Davis. The ridges framing Hospital Canyon behind the Fort are of Sleeping Lion Formation. The unit is 210 feet (65 m) of gray porphyritic rhyolite lava. The unit has columnar jointing and characteristic hoodoos (formed by weathering of columns) that can be viewed from the Davis Mountain State Park Ridge Road.

Road log from Fort Davis to Davis Mountain State Park Ridge Road

0.0   Junction of State Highway 17 and State Highway 118. Go west on State Highway 118.

0.5   Lavas flows of the Sleeping Lion Formation. There is typical weathering of columnar jointing in this part of Lympia Creek Canyon. The vertical joints are hexagonal sets common in lava flows. They develop the hexagonal pattern as the flow cools. The vertical spires are called **hoodoos.**

2.8   Turn left into Davis Mountain State Park. The exposures along the road in the park are of the Barrel Springs Formation.

3.2   Turn left to Skyline Scenic Drive.

6.8   Overlook of Hospital Canyon and Fort Davis. Another view of hoodoos eroded in the Sleeping Lion Formation, which is overlain here by the basal section of the Barrel Springs Formation.

Recommend a return to the top of the hill along Scenic Drive and **a leisurely stroll down to the park visitor center.** Road cuts expose many types of extrusive rocks in mudflows. Many contain very large blocks of lava and volcanic bombs of every size. There are several forms and colors of obsidian (volcanic glass) and interbedded ash beds. In several places there has been hydrothermal alteration of rocks and ash to white clays. There are also some deposits of chalcedony. This area undoubtedly had geysers and other types of hot springs during the cooling period after deposition of these extrusive volcanic rocks.

Extrusive Centers of the Northern Davis Mountains

As one enters the Davis Mountains from the northeast on State Highway 17 the first massive feature seen is Star Mountain (DM Figure 16). The Star Mountain Formation extrusives exposed in the cliffs, along with the Crossen Trachyte of the Alpine area and Bracks Rhyolite of areas 30 km west of the Davis Mountains are rhyolite to quartz trachyte lavas extruded from 37.38 to 36.73 m.y. ago that form regional units encompassing and extending well beyond the Davis Mountains (Trans-Pecos Figure 5, Henry and others, 1986 and1994). **Total volume of lava could exceed 1,000 km^3. They are the most prominent examples of flood rhyolites in Texas.** The Star Mountain Formation and Crossen Trachyte form a continuous belt in the eastern Davis Mountains. These lavas probably erupted from fissure vents scattered throughout their distribution.

Scenic Loop

There is a 45-mile Scenic Loop in the Davis Mountains west from Fort Davis on State Highway 118, south on State Highway 166 through the Central Davis Mountains, and then east to return on Highway State 166 (DM Figure 1). This loop takes one by beautiful outcrops of many kinds of rock and structures that result from intrusive and extrusive phenomena in a volcanic field. The loop also passes McDonald Observatory and Davis Mountains State Park. There are several delightful picnic and camping areas.

An excellent road log for this loop has been prepared by D. O. Nelson and K. L. Nelson and published in the West Texas Geological Society's 1986 Fieldtrip Guidebook (Pause and Spears, 1986, p. 67-72). The discussion here is limited to an especially interesting area in the western part of the loop.

Davis Mountains Table 1.
Geologic column for west part of Scenic Loop and symbols on DM Figure 19

Eocene Rocks			
Intrusive rocks			
	Tcl	Chlorite Latite	dikes and small stocks
	Ttd	Trachyte	dikes
	Tqm	Quartz syenite	dikes,sills and stocks
	Tqt	Quartz trachyte	sills
	Tl	Latite	small stocks
	Tt	Trachyandesite	small stocks
Extrusive rocks			
Local origin			
	Trt	Rhyolite-trachyte undifferentiated	several different lithologies
	bm	Brooks Mountain Formation	brown porphyritic trachyte
	Tgc	Goat Canyon Formation	gray to green trachyte
	Tmm	Medley Formation	brown to red-brown porphyry
	Tsi	Silicified rocks	white to gray hydrothermally altered rocks
	Period of hydrothermal activity; silicification and formation of clay minerals		
From sources outside this area			
	Tj	Jones Formation	black basalt
	Twc-bs Wild Cherry Formation, Twc, and Barrel Springs Formation, TbsIncludes interbedded Ter-Eppenauer Ranch (basalts) and Tml-Mount Locke Formations Mainly gray to red to purple rhyolites		
	Tm	Merrill Formation	brown to red-brown porphyry
	Tsp	Sheep Pasture Formation	gray to red to purple rhyolites
	Tur	Upper Rhyolite	
	Tlr	Lower Rhyolite	
Cretaceous rocks			
	Kf	Finley (?) Limestone	contact metamorphic marble
	Kc	Cox (?) Sandstone	contact metamorphic quartzite

DM Figure 16. Looking north from State Highway 17 at lava flows exposed in cliffs of Star Mountain.

DM Figure 17. Hoodoos eroded in exposures of the Limpia Formation along State Highway 17 northeast of Fort Davis. This quartz trachyte lava flow originated 36.46 m.y. ago from a source southeast of Fort Davis.

The Buckhorn extrusive center, 10 miles northwest of McDonald Observatory, formed 36.8 m.y. ago and was the source of the Gomez Tuff, which is one of the largest ash-flow tuffs in West Texas (initial volume ~200 km^3, Parker, 1986). It is one of at least twelve calderas within the Trans-Pecos volcanic province (Trans-Pecos Figure 2). The 22 by 12 km Buckhorn caldera is interpreted to have developed along incipient ring fracture zones as the tuff was extruded. Up to 450 meters of Gomez Tuff has been measured within the caldera. The Buckhorn extrusive center apparently was short lived and now is largely covered by younger rocks.

The geologic map (DM Figure 19) covers the western part of the Scenic Loop. It is included to illustrate one of the volcanic centers mentioned in this chapter. The features identified on this map are easily viewed from Scenic Loop State Highways 166/118. As shown in Davis Mountain Table 1, there are thick sections of older extrusive rocks here that came from centers outside the area. **A great volume of the extrusive rocks that came from this center has been removed by erosion. This volcanic center was the source of the youngest extrusive rocks of the Davis Mountains**.

During the intrusive phase of igneous activity, the older volcanic rocks were intensely faulted. There were stocks, sills, dikes, and probably small laccoliths, all of which caused local uplifts. Of special interest is the **White Hills xenolithic block (carried up by magma) of Cretaceous rocks**. The limestones and sandstones in this block were altered by heat and pressure of the magmas (contact metamorphism) to marbles and quartzite, respectively. The light color of the metamorphic rocks makes a striking contrast with the more drab colors of the surrounding igneous rocks.

DM Figure 18. Looking southwest from Loop Highway 166 at Sawtooth Mountain, a very thick (1,000 feet?) southwest-dipping sill of quartz microsyenite.

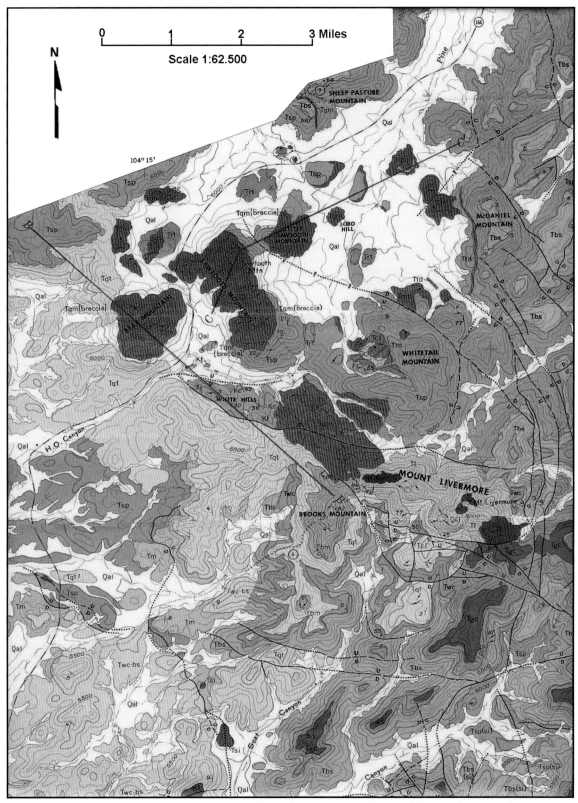

DM Figure 19. Geologic Map of western part of Scenic Loop. This is one of the Davis Mountains centers of igneous intrusive and extrusive activity. Near the middle of the map there are small outcrops of Cretaceous rocks that have been carried up and metamorphosed from limestone to marble and sandstone to quartzite by the heat of contact with the rising magmas (from Anderson, 1968).

134

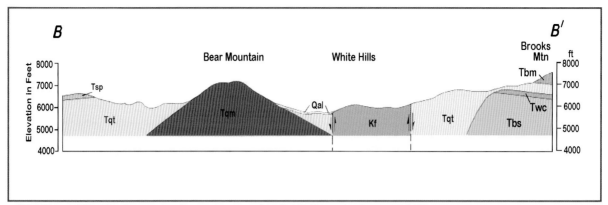

DM Figure 20. Northwest-southeast cross section B-B' (from Anderson, 1968).

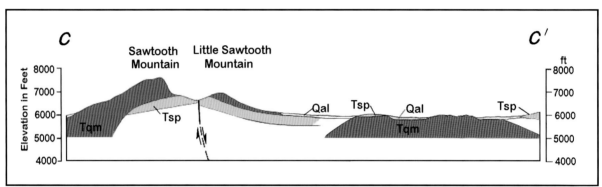

DM Figure 21. Southwest-northeast cross section C-C' (from Anderson, 1968).

DM Figure 22. Silicified tuff: White hydrothermally altered tuff exposed in southwest part of Scenic Loop.

Chapter 9
Big Bend Area

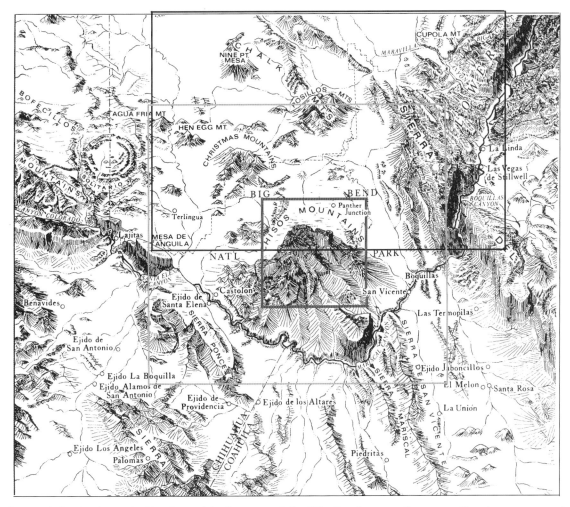

Big Bend (BB) Figure 1. Physiographic features of the Big Bend area. Orange outline is area cover by southern satellite image, BB Figure 2 and red outline is area of northern satellite image, BB Figure 8. Lavender outline is geologic map of Chisos Mountain area. Physiography by Metcalfe and Clark, 1979.

The **Big Bend area** is the southernmost tip of the Trans-Pecos region where the Rio Grande River makes a deep southward bend. Most of the area is in **Big Bend National Park**. **It is a geologist's paradise.** A visit is a delight for the variety of wild scenery, flora and the many fascinating landforms. Add to that knowledge of the **many different types of geologic features that are exposed with a minimum of vegetative cover** in this desert and the fascination of the Big Bend compounds.

The areas covered in this chapter and Chapter 10 are national and state parks. Please remember that we can look, hike, and photograph, but not collect any thing, including rocks.

Big Bend Table 1

Rock strata exposed in the Big Bend Area		
Qal Alluvium		
QTog Gravel and silt		
Oligocene		
Tsr	South Rim Formation	
Tbmr	Burro Mesa Riebeckite Rhyolite	youngest lava, 29.1 m.y.)
Tlmr	Lost Mine Rhyolite	
Twsf	Wasp Spring Flow Breccia	
Tbr	Brown rhyolitic lavas	Tbr] of Maxwell, et al, 1967. Pine Canyon Rhyolite [Tpcr] of Ogley, 1979
Eocene		
Tch	Chisos Formation	
Ttmt	Tule Mountain Trachyandesite	
Tul	Undifferentiate lavas	
Tmet	Mule Ear Spring Tuff	
Tbmb	Bee Mountain Basalt	
Tasb	Ash Spring Basalt	
Tacb	Alamo Creek Basalt	(42-38 m.y.)
Tcf	Canoe Formation	Conglomerate, tuff, local lavas
Early Tertiary Formations		
Thh	Harrold Hill Formation	Varicolored shale with channel sandstones.
Tbp	Black Peaks Formation	Gray to yellow sandstone with a basal conglomerate. Cretaceous
Upper Cretaceous		
Kjf	Javelina Formation	non-marine clay and sandstone.
Kag	Aguja Formation	non-marine clay and sandstone.
Kpf	Pen Formation	marine shale
Kbo	Boguillas Formation	light gray. chalky
Lower Cretaceous		
Kbu	Buda Limestone	
Kdr	Del Rio Clay	
Kse	Santa Elena Limestone	
Ksp	Sue Peaks Formation	calcareous shale
Kdc	Del Carmen Limestone	
Ktc	Telephone Canyon Formation	marly limestone
Kgr	Glen Rose Limestone	
angular unconformity		
Paleozoic		
Pu	**Paleozoic Formations**	undivided

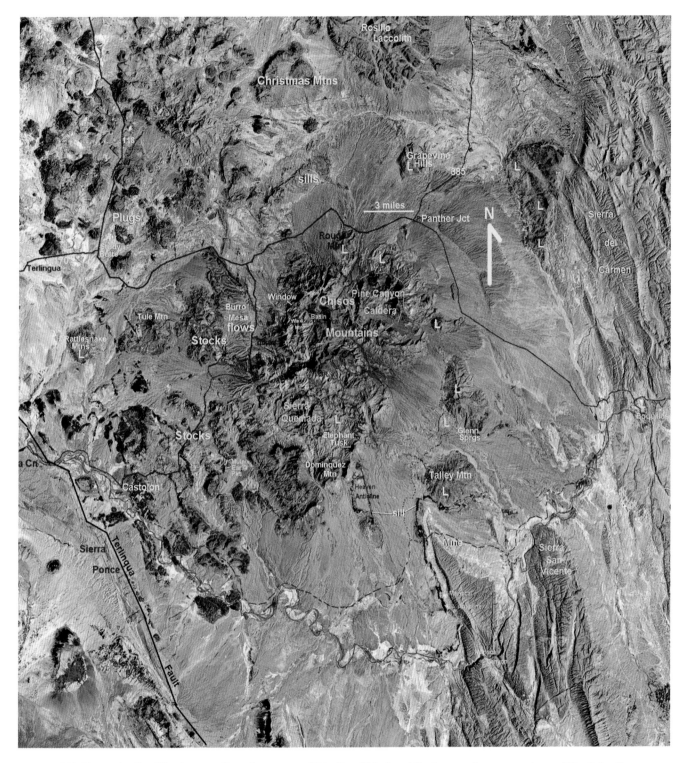

BB Figure 2. Satellite image of southern part of Big Bend National Park area. Image courtesy of Dr. John C. Dohrenwend, Southwest Satellite Imaging, (email: Dohrenwend@rkymtnhi.com). Please see north arrow and scale posted near Panther Junction.

Stratigraphy of Big Bend

A wide variety of sedimentary, extrusive volcanic and intrusive igneous rocks are exposed in the Big Bend area. The span of time represented by the rocks is from Early Paleozoic to Recent. The total thickness of sedimentary and extrusive volcanic rocks is over 14,000 feet. The Paleozoic comprises 1,400+ feet, Lower Cretaceous 2,000 feet, Upper Cretaceous 3,100 feet, Tertiary 7,300 feet, and the more recent alluvium over 500 feet.

Paleozoic Era. Paleozoic rocks occur in two places: at the north edge of the area as the southern exposures of the Marathon Uplift, and west of the Big Bend in the center of a large laccolith: the Solitario. There is also an exposure of metamorphosed Paleozoic sedimentary rocks in the Sierra Del Carmen escarpment five miles southeast of Boquillas, Coahuila, Mexico. The Paleozoic rocks underlying Big Bend are part of the Ouachita Trend, which includes highly faulted and folded limestones, novaculites, sandstones and shales that originally were deposited in a deep marine trough. This trough was subsequently squeezed between the North American plate and another to the southeast. During Late Paleozoic time sediments of the trough were thrust to the northwest and were folded into complex series of anticlines and synclines. A subsequent long period of erosion removed much of the mountain system.

Mesozoic Era. Sedimentary rocks deposited during the Cretaceous Period overlie the Paleozoic rocks unconformably. The missing Mesozoic (Triassic and Jurassic) section is absent either because of non-deposition or pre-Cretaceous erosion.

The **Lower Cretaceous** rocks **are** predominantly **thick sections of marine massive limestone**, with minor amounts of nodular limestone, marl and clay rocks. There is a thin basal conglomerate or conglomeratic sandstone. The **sequence occurs extensively in the upthrown blocks** along the eastern and western side of the park. In the "Sunken Block" (please see Miocene discussion below) of the middle of the Big Bend area Lower Cretaceous limestones are exposed in the cores of the larger anticlines. There was a period at the end of the Lower Cretaceous when this area was above sea level and was subaerially eroded (an erosional unconformity).

The **Upper Cretaceous rocks** include flaggy argillaceous limestone, chalk, clay, bentonitic clay (layers of altered volcanic ash), and sandstone. The **lower two-thirds of this section are marine** sediments and **the upper third is non-marine**. The Upper Cretaceous rocks crop out over much of the sunken block. The bentonitic clays and occasional tuffaceous sandstones occur in both the marine and non-marine sediments. The source of this volcanic material was probably some distance to the west.

Cenozoic Era. **Early Tertiary sediments** are non-marine sandstones and shales like those of the Late Cretaceous. They are only preserved in the eastern half of the Sunken Block. This is an excellent area for studying the transition from dinosaur-bearing to mammal-dominated faunas.

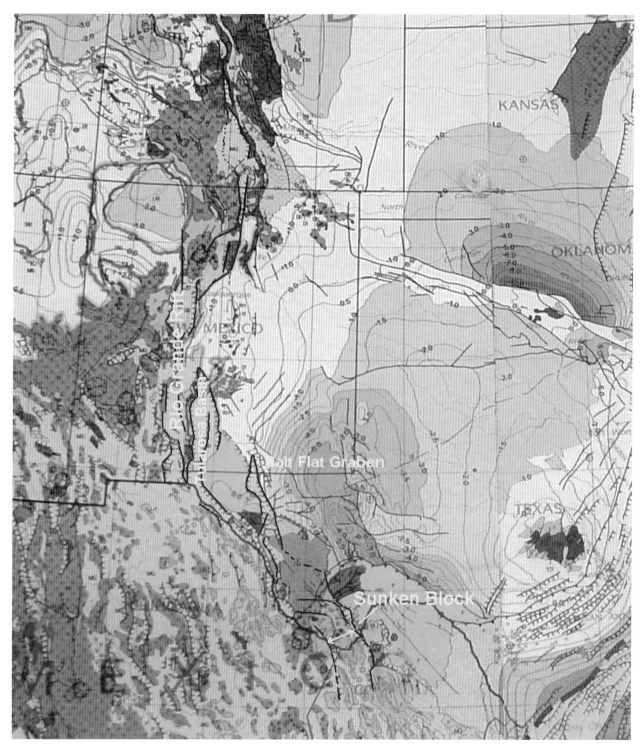

BB Figure 3. Part of Tectonic Map of North America with three *en echelon* rifts outlined (after Muehlberger, 1992).

During early Tertiary time there are three major periods of igneous activity, the products of which have been assigned to the **Eocene Canoe and Chisos Formations and the Oligocene South Rim Formation**. Each period included local uplifts caused by the emplacement of intrusive igneous bodies and outpourings from volcanoes of lava, tuffs, and ash. Contemporaneously, there was deposition of reworked sediments (conglomerates, sandstones, and clays) eroded from the volcanoes and structures uplifted by the intrusions.

Miocene to Holocene

Miocene: Continents might appear to be indestructible, but when tectonic forces uplift an area and cause blocks of crust to pull in different directions eventually the crust of a continent will crack. This causes **rifts**, which are long, linear down-dropped features. The Red Sea and the rifts of East Africa were formed in this manner. On the North American continent, a series of rift valleys developed *en echelon* in Miocene time from south of Big Bend to north of Leadville Colorado. The part of the rift system in the Big Bend National Park is called the **"Sunken Block"** (BB Figure 3).

During the Late Tertiary (from Early Miocene time on**), broad uplift of the area and the accompanying rifting resulted in the removal by erosion of thousands of feet of rock**. Many cubic miles of eroded rock material was transported by the Rio Grande to the Gulf of Mexico basin.

It was during this time that the course of the Rio Grande was **superimposed** (eroded down into = entrenched) across uplifted blocks and anticlines. By the end of the Oligocene Epoch, the Big Bend area was covered by volcanic debris of all kinds that was extremely thick and extended far beyond the present distribution. Some have estimated that the cover was five times the thickness we see today. River systems were established draining generally from west to east with some major bends around the primary extrusive centers. As the area was uplifted, the rivers became entrenched (deepened their channels) and continued to follow the same course as layer upon layer of volcanic debris, and then underlying sediments, were stripped away by erosion. In this manner, the rivers were superimposed to follow previous courses over structurally low and high areas. Thus, we now see deep canyons cutting across mountains of hard limestone and wonder why they didn't take the easy way around one end or the other of the mountain trend.

Santa Elena and Mariscal Canyons are prime examples of superimposed streams. Even the meanders from the earlier history of the river have been preserved. This kind of superposition is common throughout the Southern Rocky Mountains as the entire region has a similar history of (1) basin-filling Eocene and Oligocene sedimentation; (2) uplift starting in early Miocene time accompanied by high rates of erosion; and (3) resulting superposition of rivers across uplifted mountains. Small patches of gravels in the eastern part of the Sunken Block contain Miocene fossils. These are remnants of the original blanket. The sands and gravels of the pediments (long slopes from the foot of the mountains to the river) that are common throughout the park are relatively recent. Examination of these stream deposits will reveal that they are deposited primarily during flash floods.

Many stratified rocks of Big Bend contain fossils. Marine invertebrates, mainly ammonites, pelecypods (clams), and gastropods (snails) occur in Lower and early Late Cretaceous sediments. Dinosaur bones and teeth, turtle and crocodile remains, shark teeth, fish bones, and fossil wood occur in the Late Cretaceous non-marine deposits. Mammalian remains have been found in some Tertiary formations.

Sequence of Important Events in the Big Bend area

The structural and volcanic events of the Big Bend are: (in order of superposition)

4. Miocene and Pliocene (and possibly continuing today) regional uplift and resulting collapse of the "Sunken Block", that is, formation of a rift north-south though the area.
3. Oligocene intrusive and extrusive igneous activity – South Rim Formation.
2. Late Eocene intrusive and extrusive igneous activity – Canoe and Chisos Formations.
1. Early Eocene Laramide tectonic events.

Laramide Orogeny

The Laramide Orogeny is a time of mountain building in the western part of the North American continent that extended from 80 to 50 million years ago. The Rocky Mountains were formed during this time. In areas like Wyoming or Colorado, one mountain range would pop up and then another, gradually culminating in the complex of mountains and intervening basins that comprise the Rocky Mountains.

In the Big Bend area, Laramide tectonic activity was of a more subdued type. Big Bend Figure 2 is a satellite image that covers the central and southern parts of Big Bend National Park. Of special interest on this image is the clear view of **Cow Heaven, Mariscal, and Sierra San Vicente anticlines** in the southeast part of the picture. These spectacular structures were formed during the later part of the Laramide period of tectonism (formation of mountains, ranges, and basins). They were the result of compression of the earth's crust along the east end of the Tascotal Block. This block will be discussed further in the Big Bend Ranch State Park chapter. The north continuation of this anticlinal trend from the Cow Heaven Anticline is covered by younger extrusive rocks and obscured by intrusive features north of the Chisos Mountains.

The northwest trending anticlines in what is now the Sunken Block formed during a later phase of Laramide activity. Laramide folding and faulting also occurred in the Sierra Del Carmen and the Santiago Range. The exact time of Laramide folding in the Big Bend area is not apparent. Detailed published information (Maxwell, 1979) on the sequence of rocks in the park shows that the late Paleocene and early Eocene time sections are missing. The anticlinal folds are believed to have developed then. There is an angular unconformity between the nonvolcanic Hannold Hill Formation (Lower Eocene) and the basal volcanic units (Middle Eocene) near the northeast edge of the central anticlines that may represent the last pulse (BB Table 1). The Hannold Hill Formation has channel conglomerates that contain chert and novaculite pebbles, but none of the thick sections of coarse sediment that was eroded from the uplifted features has been identified.

There are prominent black gabbro sills that intrude the middle part of the Cretaceous section on the flanks of Mariscal and Cow Heaven Anticlines. They are easily seen as black bands around the folds on the satellite image. Earlier work dated the intrusives at 80 to 60 m.y. and had them folded along with the rest of the sedimentary section. Recent work by Harlan, et al, 1995 calculated a date of 37.0 m.y. and has them intruded well after the folding took place. Figuring out the mechanics of emplacement of intrusive sills in such a selected part of the sedimentary column over such a wide area is a real challenge.

Visitors to the Park rarely see these anticlines. A hike to the South Rim of the Chisos Mountains provides an excellent overview of these structures and other features along and south of the Rio Grande. The River Road from Castolon to near Boquillas provides access for those with high-clearance vehicles. If you try any other road in this area you will need high-clearance and four-wheel drive. A copy of the Geologic Map for the Big Bend available in Guidebook 7, Texas Bureau of Economic Geology, or Guidebook 72-59, West Texas Geological Society, will identify the outcrops and especially those that are famous for fossils. Marine invertebrates are common in the Upper Cretaceous marine rocks above the massive limestones of the cores of the anticlines. Dinosaur bones and teeth, turtle and crocodile remains, shark teeth, fish bones, and fossil wood occur in Late Cretaceous terrestrial strata. Mammalian remains are found in some Tertiary formations here and in the northeast part of the Sunken Block. **Of course, you can look and admire, but not collect.**

Igneous Episodes

The distribution and chemistry of igneous rocks intruded and extruded in successive stages of activity from middle Eocene to the end of the Oligocene time in the Big Bend area indicates they were all derived from a **very large parent magma underlying the entire area**. The chemistry of the magma progressively changed from basic to include acidic melts over about 12 million years. This suggests a deep-seated origin for the magma near the top of the mantle that moved upward, assimilating acidic rocks as it became shallower and younger. Any upward movement caused uplift and erosion-either local or regionally. Periodically, large bubbles of molten rock rose in **diapiric** fashion (upward movement of a glob of magma because it is lighter than the rocks being penetrated) above all parts of the parent magma. Some broke through to the surface and resulted in volcanic outpourings, others did not. Some rose part way and spread out as sills or laccoliths between layers of sediment, others formed plugs. The intrusions [*Ig* on maps] caused uplift and tilting of overlying strata, which in turn caused erosion so that in each stage clastic rocks are interbedded with pyroclastic rocks (ash tuffs, welded tuffs = ignimbrites, volcanic mud flows = lahars, debris flows) and lava flows.

Intrusive Features Northwest of Chisos Mountains

Traveling west out of the Park on State Highway 118 and in the vicinity of Study Butte there are many dark-colored rocky buttes and mountains cored by igneous rock. The age of these intrusive rocks is between 47 to 39 m.y. and they are contemporaneous with the extrusive rocks of Canoe Formation. These are bodies of intrusive magma that rose to a shallow depth (possibly as shallow as 2,000 feet (640 m) from the surface). Some may have broken through to the surface and fed the extrusive rocks of the Canoe Formation. They are usually plug-like (cylindrical), but some may be laccolithic. They measure from a few hundred feet to six miles in diameter. The rock types range from mafic to very felsic silicic (T-P Table 1 is a description of igneous rocks). Because of the wide range of rock types, these intrusive features are interpreted to have moved upward from different parts of the underlying Chisos area parent magma (Please see BB Figure 29 in the Maverick Road Log.).

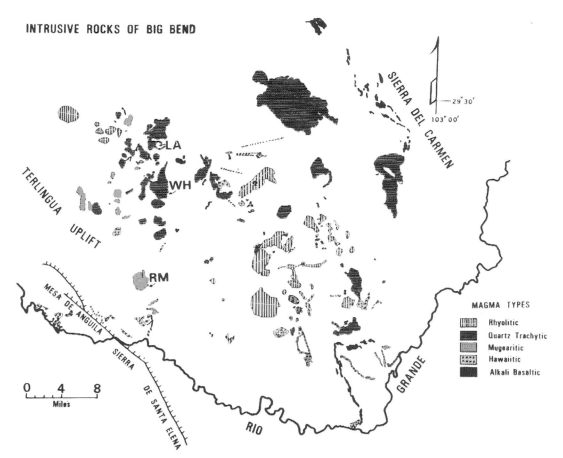

BB Figure 4. Intrusive rocks of the Big Bend area (Indest and Carman, 1979).

Quicksilver Deposits of the Terlingua District

This mercury mining district extends east from just south of the Solitario to east of Study Butte. It was active from 1900 to 1946, and produced over 150,000 flasks of mercury (76 pounds each). There were about 20 mines and many prospects. More than 90 percent of the mercury came from the Chisos-Rainbow and Mariposa mines near Terlingua and the Study

Butte mine east of Study Butte. The geology is a combination of Laramide folds and faults that were intruded by middle Eocene domes and plugs. Mercury is found in veins as well as sheet-like and pipelike bodies in both sedimentary and igneous rocks. Cinnabar is the principal ore mineral. The mercury was deposited at a depth of about 2,000 feet below the surface (at the time of deposition) by hydrothermal (hot water) solutions ascending through breccia pipes and fractures (Yates and Thompson, 1952). Breccia pipes result from vertical blowouts of volcanic gas. The breccia is the broken pieces of rock that fills the pipes after the blowout.

Extrusive and intrusive rocks of the Chisos Mountain Area

The first episode of volcanic activity in the Big Bend area was during the Middle Eocene and is recorded in rocks assigned to the **Canoe Formation.** The basal beds of this formation are yellowish, conglomeratic sandstone that contains pebbles of novaculite (a silica rock), chert, and igneous rock. Most of the 1,160-foot thick formation is clay that includes increasing amounts of tuff (volcanic ash) in the upper part. Locally, the section includes basalt lava flows. Mammalian remains accurately date the Canoe Formation as middle Eocene.

The **Late Eocene Chisos Formation** conformably overlies the Canoe Formation with no clear break. In the Chisos Mountains, the formation includes 3,438 feet of massive coarse conglomerate, coarse-grained sandstone, fine-to-medium-grained tuffaceous sandstone, tuff, indurated (welded) tuff, and lava. South, west, and northwest of the Chisos Mountains the sequence includes some lavas that only have limited extent and **four widespread flows and one indurated tuff bed** that have distinguishing characteristics (please see BB Table 1).

In many areas, the Alamo Creek Basalt lies directly on eroded beds of the Cretaceous Javelina Formation. The five members are interbedded with variable thicknesses of tuffaceous clay, tuff, coarse massive conglomerates, and some fresh water limestone.

Basalt sills dated at 37.0 m.y. (late Eocene) were intruded into the middle of the Cretaceous rocks in the anticlines southeast of the Chisos Mountains. The outcrops of these sills can be seen on Big Bend Figure 3. Please also see the discussion in the River Road log, Mile Points 29.6 to 31.1.

Sierra Quemada, a collapse feature southwest of the Chisos Mountains, along with Dominguez Mountain were the main sources of Chisos Formation extrusive rocks. Sierra Quemada was the source of the Mule Ear Spring Tuff (31.5 m.y.), which is the earliest ignimbrite (welded tuff) in the Chisos Mountains region (Ogley, 1979).

The Maverick and Ross Maxwell Drive road logs include additional discussions of exposures of extrusive and some intrusive rocks of the Chisos Formation

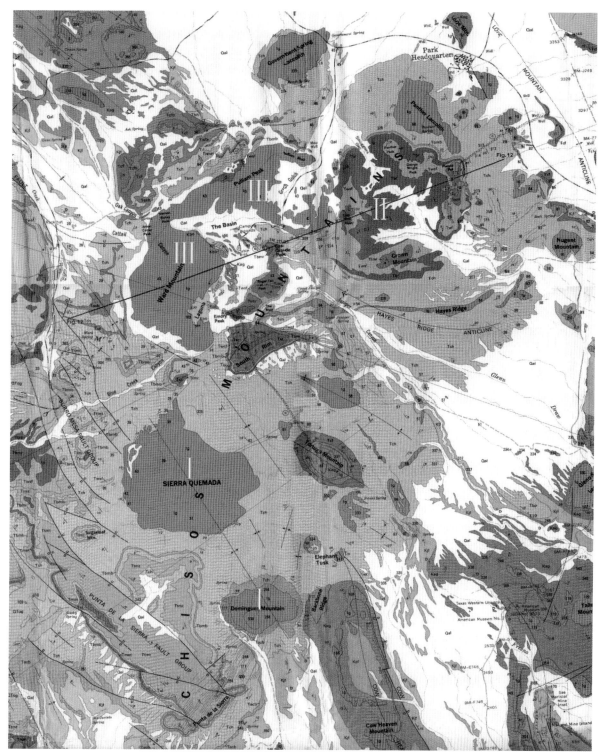

BB Figure 5. Geologic Map of the Chisos Mountains showing volcanic centers. **I**, Sierra Quemada and Dominguez Mountain, primary sources of the extrusive rocks of the Chisos Formation; **II**, Pine Canyon volcano, primary source of the extrusive rocks of the South Rim Formation, with its caldera and ring dike system; and **III**, the plug-like intrusions of Ward to Pulliam Mountains. The plug-like intrusions (I) have the same composition as the Burro Mesa Rhyolite (youngest lava flow of the Chisos Formation) and are contemporaneous with the last emanations from the parent magma. Red line shows the location of cross section on BB Figure 12 (from Maxwell, 1979).

The **Oligocene South Rim Formation** is the youngest volcanic unit of Big Bend Park. The formation consists of thick lavas, flow breccia units, tuff and other pyroclastic rocks, and conglomerate. The primary source was the Pine Canyon volcano of the northeast part of the Chisos Mountains. The South Rim Formation is most extensively distributed in the central Chisos Mountains where the formation is over 1,000 feet thick (BB Table 1 and BB Figures 6 and 7).

The base of the formation everywhere rests on an erosion surface cut on older rocks ranging in age from Cretaceous to the upper part of the Eocene Chisos Formation. The erosional angular unconformity is probably the result of domal uplift of the area by upward movement of the parent magma.

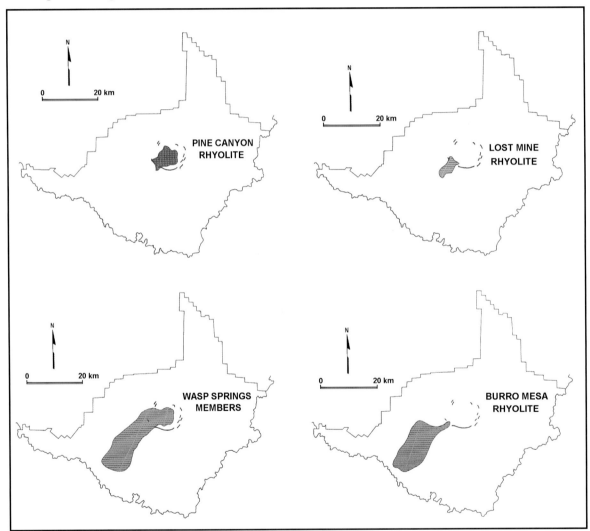

BB Figure 6. Generalized distribution of the four members of the South Rim Formation. The preservation to the southwest is likely the result of erosion and no preservation of extrusives distributed in the other directions. The ring dike around the edge of the Pine Canyon Caldera is shown in black (From Ogley, 1979).

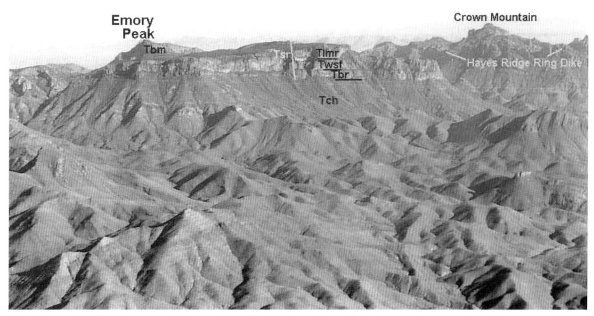

BB Figure 7. View from an airplane of the South Rim of the Chisos Mountains showing the type section of the lower three members of the South Rim Formation. The upper member, the Burro Mesa riebeckite rhyolite flow, is exposed in the high slopes of Emery Peak. The Hayes Ridge Ring Dike is at the southwest edge of the Pine Canyon Caldera. Crown Mountain is in the southern part of the caldera. Tch= Chisos Formation. South Rim Formation (Tsr) Members in ascending order: Tbr= Brown (Pine Canyon) Rhyolite; Twsf= Wasp Spring flow breccia; Tlmr= Lost Mine Rhyolite; Tbm= Burro Mesa Riebeckite Rhyolite. Photo by Bruce Blake.

The extrusive units of the **South Rim Formation in and southwest of the Chisos Mountains are prominently in view** on the ridges of the east side of The Basin and along Ross Maxwell Drive. The sequence of events and the distribution of these rocks is enumerated by David S, Ogley (1979) to include (oldest to youngest):

1. Rising magma domed an area centering at the Pine Canyon Volcano (northeastern part of the Chisos Mountains) and resulted in widespread erosion of the Chisos and older formations.
2. Simultaneous extrusion of the Pine Canyon Rhyolite (an ash-flow tuff) and initial collapse of the caldera of the volcano. The thickness of the Pine Canyon Rhyolite is 1,000 feet (300 m.) in the center and effectively 0 outside the caldera.
3. The Wasp Spring Member is characterized by an outflow that is a poorly to densely welded ash-flow tuff.
4. The Lost Mine Rhyolite is a series of ash-flow units with limited distribution.
5. The Burro Mesa Rhyolite was the result of a return to more volatile conditions like that of the Wasp Springs Member. The ash-flow and ignimbrite units of the Burro Mesa Member spread out to the southwest.
6. The further collapse of the caldera during extrusion of the Burro Mesa Member resulted in the intrusion of a ring dike around part of the collapsed area (Hayes Ridge Ring Dike) and a number of dikes that trend southwest from the caldera. The Burro

Mesa riebeckite rhyolite capping Emory Peak and the upper flow capping Burro Mesa are lava flows from the Hayes Ridge Ring Dike. The lava that caps Casa Grande came from the southwest-trending dikes (Ogley, 1979, p. 68).

7. The emplacement of the large Ward Mountain-Pulliam Peak granitic plug west of the caldera appears to be one of the last emanations from the parent magma (labeled III on BB Figure 5, please also see BB Figures 14 and 16). Chemically these intrusive rocks are very similar to the Burro Mesa riebeckite rhyolite.

The repetitive pattern of eruptions suggests a cyclic process. A single cycle consists of the eruption of a series of ash-flows with low volatile content accompanied by sagging of the caldera floor. After an eruption the vent becomes choked allowing the underlying magma to become enriched in volatiles. At a critical volatile pressure a classic eruption occurs, venting a highly mobile ash-flow unit. After the eruption the cycle is repeated.

The Sunken Block

Near the end of igneous activity in the Trans-Pecos Region this part of the continent was subjected to major changes. Apparently there was a widespread uplift that centered on the southern Rocky Mountain area and affected a broad area from eastern Kansas to Nevada. The amount of uplift is not known and the subject of a lot of speculation. Accompanying the uplift was the formation of a series of north-south rifts. There are three major rift valleys that extend *en echelon* from south of Big Bend to north of Leadville, Colorado (BB Figure 3). This was a time of major structural change. The broad uplift rejuvenated (uplifted) the mountain areas and resulted in high rates of erosion in the mountains and high rates of sedimentation from the mountain fronts to the Gulf of Mexico basin.

The Sunken Block is bound on the east by a continuous mountain trend from the Santiago Mountains to the Sierra Del Carmen. The west side shifts from the Terlinqua Fault at the east side of the Mesa de Anquilla to the Chalk Draw Fault in the northern part of Big Bend National Park (BB Figures 3 and 8). In other words, it is the down-dropped area between uplifted features on either side.

BB Figure 8. False color satellite image of northern part of Big Bend National Park. Image was provided by Dr. John C. Dohrenwend and his company, Southwest Satellite Imaging (dohrenwend@rkymtnhi.com). Please note north arrow and scale posted near park headquarters.

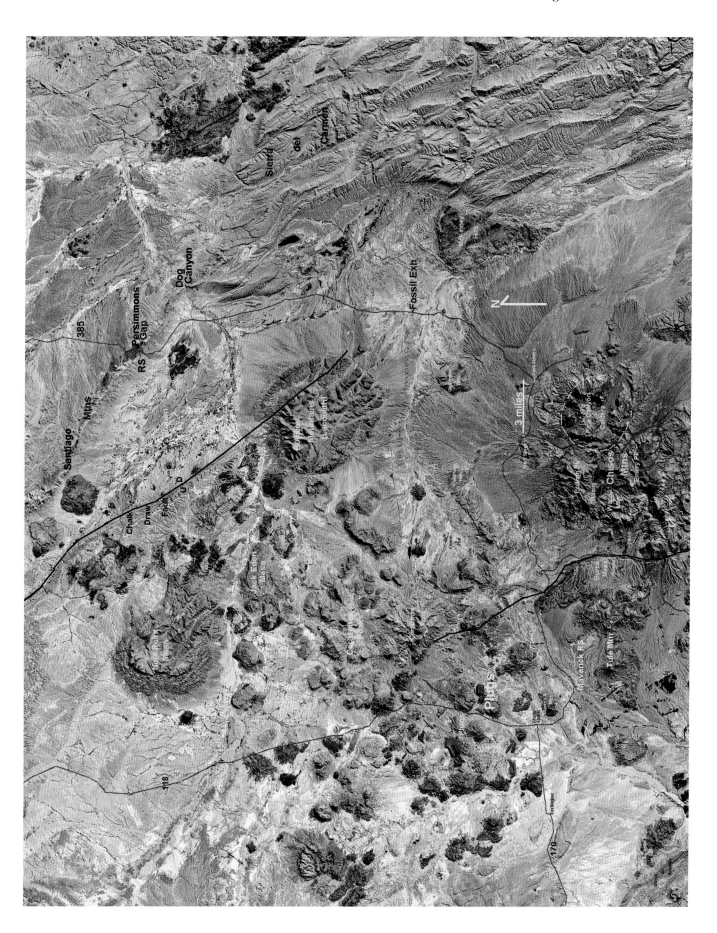

Big Bend National Park Roads

US Highway 385 from North Entrance to Panther Junction

Most visitors enter the park by traveling south on US Highway 385 from Marathon, Texas. The rocks and structures of the Marathon Uplift are fascinating for their own peculiarities (Chapter 2). At the southern edge of this geologic province, the highway rises through a gap in the Santiago Mountain chain and suddenly, at the northern entrance to the park, the entire character of the landscape changes. Drive slowly through the gap (Persimmon Gap) as the hillsides show vestiges of highly deformed Lower Paleozoic rocks overlain by Lower Cretaceous limestones, both of which are further deformed. The combination assumes weird angles because of complex local post-Cretaceous faulting in the Santiago Mountain chain.

About four miles southeast from Persimmon Gap along this ridge, there is another view of complex structures in the walls of Dog Canyon. If the road from the highway is not open, then it is about a 1.3-mile hike to Dog Canyon. It is well worth the effort as there are spectacular views of folded and faulted rocks in the canyon.

Descending from Persimmon Gap, the highway crosses a fault into the Chalk Draw graben, which is the narrowest part of the Sunken Block. For the rest of the distance to Panther Junction the highway is on the eastern part of the Sunken Block. The first 15 miles are on Upper Cretaceous rocks covered by a thin veneer of alluvium. On the east are successively the Santiago, Dagger and Sierra Del Carmen Mountains, which are uplifted Lower Cretaceous limestones.

To the west of the highway are a series of structures formed by intrusions. The largest feature is the Rosillos Mountains, a very large laccolith of olivine-bearing granite. Look for the northwest-southeast Chalk Draw Fault that slices across the northeast part of the laccolith.

The 7 ½-mile side trip to Dagger Flat is designed primarily to see stands of giant dagger yuccas. It also provides an opportunity to see outcrops of the Lower Cretaceous Buda and Boquillas Formations (please see BB Table 1) in the foothills of the Sierra Del Carmen.

From a point about two miles south of the Dagger Flat turn off to near Panther Junction the highway is on non-marine early Tertiary rocks. The Fossil Bone Exhibit has casts of mammal bones excavated from the Hannold Hill and Canoe Formations in this area.

Two miles north of the junction the feature on the right (west) is the Grapevine Hills, an eroded olivine-bearing granite laccolith. A sill is exposed in the nearest jagged hills.

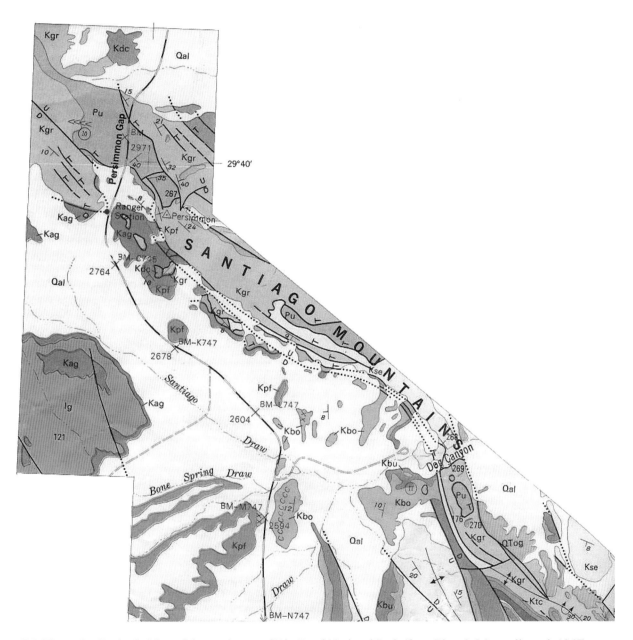

BB Figure 9. Geologic Map of the north part of Big Bend National Park (from Plate 2, Maxwell, et al, 1967).

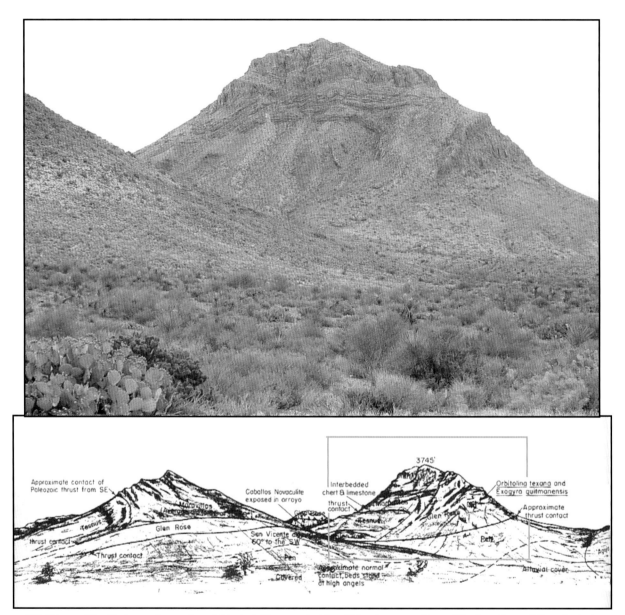

BB Figure 10. Picture of complex folds in hill on east side of Persimmons Gap. The location of the photo is shown on the accompanying sketch (from Bolden, et. al., 1972).

BB Figure 11. Picture looking east from highway at Dog Canyon plus sketch of the panorama (from Bolden, et al, 1972).

Basin Drive

The word Chisos is generally accepted to mean ghosts, spirits, or phantoms.

This seven-mile drive climbs up Green Gulch to Panther Pass (elevation 5,800 feet) in the north part of the Chisos Mountains, then drops into **The Basin**. During the climb, the rocks on the left are on the north flank of the Pine Canyon volcano. The rocks on either side of Panther Pass are at the east end of the **Ward Mountain to Pullium Peak intrusive mass.** This intrusive mass is shown on BB Figure 5. The large intrusion was emplaced contemporaneously with the last extrusions from the Pine Canyon volcano. The intrusive rocks of this large intrusive mass have the same composition as the Burro Mesa lava flows.

The Lost Mine Trail takes off to the left just west of the pass. It is a five mile round trip up the north side of the Pine Canyon volcano. There are excellent views to the north and east, so take copies of the maps and satellite photo so that you can identify features.

The Basin is a large valley eroded between the west side of the Pine Canyon volcano and the Ward Mountain to Pullium Peak intrusive mass. The intrusive mass is exposed on either side of **The Window**, an eroded notch that provides the outlet for drainage from The Basin.

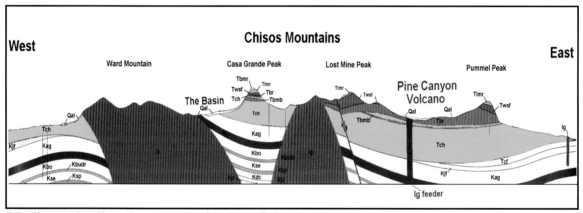

BB Figure 12. West-East cross-section through Ward Mountain, The Basin, Casa Grande, and the Pine Canyon volcano. The intrusive mass on the section between Casa Grande and Pine Canyon volcano is the southeast end of the Ward Mountain to Pulliam Peak intrusive. Cross-section line is posted on BB Figure 5 (after Maxwell, 1972. cross section D-D').

BB Figure 13 illustrates the geology exposed on the west flank of Casa Grande. The lower half of the slope has a Chisos Formation section that was extruded from the Sierra Quemada volcano (please see BB Figure 5). The upper slope has South Rim Formation lava flows and other extrusives from the Pine Canyon volcano immediately to the east of the mountain. The rocks of the ridge that bounds The Basin from Casa Grande to Emory Peak likewise came from the Pine Canyon volcano. BB Figure 7 shows the section of the South Rim lavas and flow breccias preserved southwest of the Pine Canyon volcano.

Chisos Basin is a delightful site for hiking, camping, and enjoying the scenery. To the west, The Window frames a gorgeous sunset every evening. There are a number of hiking trails from the Basin. The best hiking trail is the 13 mile round trip to the **South Rim** where exceptional vistas of the Big Bend and adjacent parts of Mexico await.

BB Figure 13. Geology of the west slope of Casa Grande.

BB Figure 14. View to west of the Window and the intrusive rocks exposed around the west and north sides of The Basin. These intrusives are the youngest igneous rocks in Big Bend. They have the same composition and are either contemporaneous with or post-date the Burro Mesa Riebeckite Rhyolite flows.

BB Figure 15. View of Appetite Ridge from Basin Lodge. The name was applied during 1930's CCC projects. When someone complained about the chow he was invited to climb the ridge. Food was much better after the climb. In place or slide block? I see it as a slide block because of the steep dips of the rocks towards the slope.

BB Figure 16. Looking southwest from Basin Drive at Pulliam Peak. This solid intrusive is a continuation of those on either side of the Window.

BB Figure 17. Looking north from Basin Drive at Government Springs laccolith, which is just west of the junction with State Highway 118.

Panther Junction to Boquillas Canyon Overlook, Park Route 2

The highway curves around the northeast side of the Pine Canyon Volcano then heads southeast to Rio Grande Village and terminates at the Boquillas Canyon overlook (please see BB Figure 2). There are a number of small laccoliths east of the volcano. The highway drops down to the eastern side of the Sunken Block on Upper Cretaceous rocks that in places have a veneer of pediment gravels.

The first road to the right is the primitive Glenn Spring Road. Glenn Springs is nine miles south and was notable for its candellila wax industry of the early 1900's. Mexican bandits associated with Pancho Villa raided the settlement on Cinco de Mayo, 1916. They killed the storekeeper's nine-year-old son and three of the nine soldiers camping there at the time.

The road is passable to the River Road if you keep to the east of Talley Mountain and avoid the Black Gap road that lies west of Talley Mountain. The latter is strictly for high clearance, four-wheel drive vehicles. There are laccoliths and sills along the Glenn Springs road.

Two miles south of the highway on the Glenn Springs Road there is a parking area for the Pine Canyon Trail. This trail climbs west into the Pine Canyon volcano through **Hayes Ridge, which is a ring dike that intruded the perimeter of the caldera after the collapse of the central part of the volcano.** At the ring dike there is a **misty waterfall** that has created a local grotto surrounded by exotic vegetation. It is a place of remarkable coolness on a hot summer's day because of the natural air conditioning provided by the evaporating mist.

Back on the highway, near Rio Grande Village, it is worth the effort to find the hot springs (for soaking purposes). In this area there are excellent exposures of Upper Cretaceous rocks.

At the end of the highway is the Boquillas Canyon parking area. A trail climbs over a small ridge and drops down to the floodplain of the river. A short hike down river into the canyon takes one into the Lower Cretaceous limestones of the Sierra del Carmen. Of special interest are the metates (bedrock mortar holes) in the limestones along the riverbank. At the end of the trail are natural dunes formed by wind blowing sand up the steep slope from the riverbank. Many delight in sliding or rolling down the dunes.

BB Figure 18. View to southeast from a point 4 miles south of State Highway 118 on Ross Maxwell Drive. Three dikes (d) intrude into tuffaceous shale of the Chisos Formation. The dikes are part of a swarm that radiates from Sierra Quemada, which is about five miles farther southeast. Sierra Quemada is the primary source of the extrusive rocks that make up the Chisos Formation. Another swarm of dikes radiates from Dominguez Mountain about three miles southeast of Sierra Quemada. Dominguez Mountain is a second source area of the Chisos Formation,

BB Figure 19. View at 5.45-miles southeast at main branch of Burro Mesa fault. Chisos Formation beds are exposed on both sides of the fault. The section is down-dropped on west (right) side.

Ross Maxwell Scenic Drive, Park Route 5

This 33-mile drive to Santa Elena Canyon was laid out by Dr. Ross A. Maxwell, geologist and first superintendent of the park, and Dr. John W. Dietrich to maximize the enjoyment of the scenery and the classical geologic features of this area west and southwest of the Chisos Mountains. Please review the route on BB Figures 2 and 5.

When you turn off State Highway 118, the road is in the middle of a syncline in the Late Cretaceous Javelina Formation, which is non-marine and contains dinosaur bones. To the west and subparallel to the highway is a prominent fault along the east base of Burro Mesa. Burro Mesa is capped by the Burro Mesa Riebeckite Rhyolite lava flow, the last preserved lava from the Pine Canyon Volcano of the northeast part of the Chisos Mountains. Displacement on the fault is over 3,000 feet (Maxwell, 1979).

Mileage

0.0   Junction of State Highway 118 and Ross Maxwell Drive. Turn south on Park Route 5.

2.05   On skyline at 3:00, the bald hill on Burro Mesa is capped by the upper members of the South Rim Formation; Burro Mesa riebeckite rhyolite overlies the yellow Wasp Spring flow breccia. At 10:00, in the creek bed, the variegated clay in the Javelina Formation contains dinosaur bones.

3.55   Highway crosses a dike intruded into Chisos Formation. There is a great deal of petrified wood in the Chisos Formation of this area.

4.25   At 9:00, excellent exposures of Wasp Spring Flow Breccia.

5.45   Highway crosses a major splay of the Burro Mesa Fault (BB Figure 5).

8.9   Sotol Point Overlook. Immediately before the turnoff the highway crosses Burro Mesa fault, which has very little displacement at this point. Bee Mountain Basalt (South Rim Formation) crops out on both sides of the fault. The overlook is an excellent point to view Chisos Mountains, Burro Mesa and the west side of the Sunken Block where it is cut by the Santa Elena Canyon of the Rio Grande.

        Sotol Plants are abundant in this area, especially on north-facing slopes. They are clumps of narrow-bladed (saw-tooth edge) leaves 1 to 3 feet long. The hearts of the plant are edible. Boiled, the taste is similar to cabbage. The hearts are also used as a source of alcohol. Burro power was used to crush the plants and some think that bacteria from the burros aided fermentation.

        On returning to the highway there are Late Tertiary gravels along the road for two miles. Cobbles and boulders include a wide variety of Paleozoic, Cretaceous and Tertiary rocks.

12.6   Turnoff to Burro Spring and Burro Mesa Pouroff (park designation for a flash flood water fall).

15.9   At 9:00, Goat Mountain. There is a broad 900-foot valley on this west side of Goat Mountain that was eroded into Chisos Formation tuffs and basalts. The valley is filled with South Rim Formation Wasp Spring flow breccia overlain by Burro Mesa riebeckite rhyolite (caprock of Goat Mountain). There is a spine-like intrusion of riebeckite rhyolite into the Wasp Spring and Burro Mesa members near the lower center of the valleyfill.

17.1   Mule Ear Overlook. The Mule Ears are two local dikes intruded into upper units of the Chisos Formation. Upper members of the South Rim Formation, especially the Burro Mesa Riebeckite Rhyolite, cap the high mesa features like Kit, Round, and Goat Mountains. There are large boulders of Burro Mesa riebeckite rhyolite (BB Figure 21) around the parking area.

BB Figure 20. View southeast from overlook on Ross Maxwell Drive of the Mule Ear Peaks. Each peak is part of a dike intruded into Chisos Formation rocks.

18.3   Road cut through Alamo Creek Basalt, lowest member of the Chisos Formation. In this area it is overlain by Burro Mesa riebeckite rhyolite. Apparently the intervening members of both formations were removed by erosion before the Burro Mesa flow occurred.

20.5   There is a windmill at 3:00. At 12:00 in bluff, old gravels have been folded and now have dips as steep as 35 degrees, indicating post-Miocene deformation.

21.0   At 12:00. Cerro Castellan is cored by an intrusive igneous pipe.

22.2   Tertiary mammal bone locality in old gravel. Early Miocene camel, deer and rabbit bones have been collected.

BB Figure 21. Boulder of riebeckite rhyolite at Mule Ear Peaks overlook. **This boulder is from the youngest lava in the park**. The phenocrysts (crystals) of feldspar are easily seen. The largest is one centimeter in diameter. Hard to see, but there are also small crystals of a black wavy mineral called riebeckite. The intrusive plutons on either side of the Window in The Basin are composed of the same rock, but generally with larger crystals and a granite appearance.

23.4   There are small igneous pipes in this area.

25.0   Castolon Village. From here to Santa Elena Canyon the rocks are Cretaceous Aguja Sandstone. Locally, dikes and sills intrude the sandstone.

33.0   Santa Elena Overlook. Lower Cretaceous limestones crop out in the canyon on the upthrown side of the Terlingua Fault, which is the west side of the Sunken Block.

33.7   Santa Elena Canyon picnic ground in mesquite thicket. If you walk over 100 yards into the canyon or climb Mesa de Anguila be sure to carry sufficient water.

BB Figure 22. Eastern end of Santa Elena Canyon.

River Road

The River Road is a 51-mile primitive road, parts of which follow the Rio Grande, but much of which is a considerable distance from the river. The road requires a full day to be explored end-to-end, including side trips. Regardless of the type of vehicle you have, only traverse this road on clear dry days. Segments of the road are on clay and become impassable when wet. The other problem is flash floods, which can be extremely dangerous. There are no bridges. Check your spare tire and take plenty of water, both for your vehicle and passengers.

Mileage

0.0 (50.6 from east end) The west end takes off from the Ross Maxwell Drive 2 miles northeast of Castolon. *Some maps show a road along the river southeast from Castolon, but parts of that road were washed out in 1975.* The new junction is just north of Cerro Castellan, which is a stack of eroded lava flows of the Chisos Formation. The road continues southeast down a graben (a down-dropped block with a fault on either side) that is part of a series of northwest trending fault blocks between here and Castolon. The age of faulting is primarily Miocene, but may also include more recent movements. To the northeast, the mesas are capped by upper South Rim members, to the southwest the high features are in the Chisos Formation. The road is on old gravels from the junction to the river.

4.6   (46.0) After joining the old River Road, the road continues southeast along the north side and through the Sierra de Chino. All the rocks in these hills are members of the Chisos Formation that came from either the Sierra Quemada or Dominguez Mountain centers (BB Figure 5). Along the road near the river there are a number of northeast trending dikes, some of which continue across the river into Mexico. These dikes are part of a swarm that radiates from Dominguez Mountain, 10 miles northeast.

13.9   (36.7) the road passes a gauging station.

15.3   (35.3) You are driving through the remains of the Johnson Ranch, a combination trading post, cotton farm, and goat ranch. During the 1930's and early 40's, the US Army Air/Corps constructed a landing strip here to train pilots from San Antonio's Kelly Field. One story has it that the final test prior to graduation from the training course the pilot had to fly between the Mule Ears.

17.7 to 18.6 (32.9 to 32.0) Road is very close to river for this distance. Due north the jagged outline of Punta de la Sierra marks the southern point of the Chisos Mountains. A number of northeast-trending dikes in this highland radiate from Dominguez Mountain that is about three miles northeast of Punta de la Sierra. All the rocks of the highland are Chisos Formation. At this point, the River Road is on gravel-covered Upper Cretaceous Javelina Formation.

BB Figure 23. Looking north at Chisos Formation outcrops on Punta de la Sierra, southern highland of the Chisos Mountains. Dikes are labeled "d".

23.1   (27.5) North of the road is the Dominguez Spring trailhead. The trail leads north across the west side of the intrusive rocks of Dominguez Mountain to a spring south of Sierra Quemada. The northern end of the trail is in the heart of the earlier volcanic center. There are several reliable springs along the trail.

25.0   (25.6) Side road towards the river to Woodson's Place. It is considered the best fishing hole on the river. This is the midpoint on the River Road.

26.9   (23.7) The barrier is used to close the west end of the road in wet weather.

27.4   (23.2) On the road to south it is six miles to Talley campsite, a popular embarkation point for boat parties entering Mariscal Canyon. There is excellent hiking from the site to the top of Mariscal Mountain. Several prolific fossil layers can be found in the lower part of the Upper Cretaceous section on this west flank of Mariscal anticline. Be sure to take ample water for the hike and secure your vehicle, as theft is a recurring problem.

29.6   (21.0) Turn right to cross the north end of Mariscal anticline. The Black Gap Road straight ahead goes 8.5 miles past Talley Mountain to Glenn Springs. That road is not maintained and is very rough. As the name implies, Black Gap is a box canyon through a gabbro sill like that at the next stop.

Dinosaur remains are found in the non-marine Aguja and Javelina Formations in the park. Skeletal remains of duck-billed, horned and carnivorous dinosaurs have been found by various groups in the Fresno Creek drainage west of Black Gap.

BB Figure 24.   Looking northwest from Black Gap junction at north end of Cow Heaven Anticline and Elephant Tusk. Prominent ridge around Cow Heaven anticline is the gabbro sill. Elephant Tusk is an intrusive stock that may have fed a volcano at one time.

The sharp ridges on either side of Cow Heaven anticline are a gabbro sill intruded into the middle of the Upper Cretaceous section. One half-mile east we will stop on this same sill on the west flank of Mariscal anticline (BB Figure 25). The sill at both places is very evident on the satellite image BB Figure 2.

BB Figure 25. Looking south from stop on black gabbro sill at highest part of Mariscal anticline (please see also BB Figure 2). Anticline is eroded to top of the Lower Cretaceous massive limestone section. Mariscal Canyon cuts through the southern part of this anticline.

30.1 (20.5) **Stop** on top of the black gabbro sill (age 37.1 m.y.) and view the west flank of Mariscal anticline. This sill was emplaced after the anticline was formed (Harlan, et al, 1995). A short distance east of the sill the bedrock is flaggy limestone of the Boquillas Formation. This section is equivalent to the Austin Chalk of Central Texas.

30.5 (20.1) Rough road on the Boquillas Formation. Now crossing the north-plunging part of the Mariscal anticline.

32.0 (18.6) Mariscal Mine is up the draw on the east flank of Mariscal Mountain. Cinnabar, mercury sulphide, was discovered here in 1900. A mine (actually 24 separate mines) was developed that had many successive owners. Between 1900 and 1955, 1,400 flasks of refined mercury weighing 76 pounds each were shipped. This is nearly one-quarter of the total produced in United States.

The work of digging cinnabar ore by pick and shovel from mines in Mariscal Mountain and then heating it to render mercury was both difficult and unhealthy. Those who worked around the furnace often became "salivated", meaning they produced abnormal amounts of saliva. Most veteran furnace men had no teeth and developed chronic respiratory problems from breathing mercury fumes.

The cinnabar was found in the Boquillas Formation in proximity of a series of sills and faults. It is apparent that hydrothermal waters associated with the intrusions carried the cinnabar and precipitated it in fractures around the intrusives and in the fault zone.

34.1   (16.5) Tornillo Creek bridge. This stream drains about 350 square miles.

38.2   (12.4) South of sandstone ridge in Upper Cretaceous Aguja Formation, on the east side of the road, are some interesting clay hills veined with calcite. Watch for scattered exposures of the basalt sill a short distance north of the River Road.

39.0   (11.6) Narrow rocky wash. Good view of various desert plants including: Lechuguilla, chino grass, and purple-tinged pricklypear. Watch for candelilla.

39.6   (11.0) Flat topped mountain to the north is Talley Mountain, which is capped by a sill. West of Talley Mountain in the Aguja Formation a number of dinosaurs were excavated before the park was established.

BB Figure 26. Looking southeast at San Vicente anticline in Mexico (please see BB Figure 2).

41.0   (9.6) Road to the northwest is the Glenn Spring Road that joins the paved highway five miles east of Panther Junction. To the southeast across the river, Sierra San Vicente is another very large anticline parallel to Mariscal anticline. Both anticlines are mountains that have been eroded to expose Lower Cretaceous limestones. These folds were formed near the end of the Laramide mountain building Period (roughly 80 to 50 m.y. ago).

47.0   (3.7) Site of San Vicente, a center of population prior to establishment of the park. One mile northwest is the low relief San Vicente anticline (yes, there are two of them). This anticline on the Texas side is eroded to the Pen Formation over the crest.

48.5   (2.1) At 9:00, 100 yards, USGS benchmark, elevation 1,881 feet.

49.0   (1.6) Small dike cuts the Boquillas Formation. There are many such dikes in this part of Park.

50.1   (0.5). Limestone hills are Boquillas Formation on the west flank of Sierra Del Carmen. This is the east edge of the Sunken Block. Yellow clay at 9:00 is in Pen Formation.

50.6   (0.0). Paved highway, Park Route 2. Rio Grande Village is 5.1 miles east. Panther Junction is 15 miles west. Sandstone to right contains a marine fauna.

BB Figure 27. Candelilla near Glenn Springs.

Maverick Drive. State Highway 118 from Panther Junction to Ross Maxwell Drive Junction to Study Butte

This 25.4-mile tour through the Maverick (West) entrance is an excellent opportunity to see examples of Chihuahuan Desert vegetation with magnificent mountain backdrops. The route also has many notable geologic features.

Mileage

0.0   (25.4 miles from Study Buttes). Panther Junction.

0.2 (25.2) Service station. At 2:00, Lone Mountain, a sill of fine-grained granite that intrudes the Upper Cretaceous Aguja Formation. This hill is on the southwest flank of an anticline, most of which is buried by gravel.

2.4 (23.0) At 3:00. Grapevine Hills, an eroded olivine-bearing granite laccolith intruded into Upper Cretaceous rocks.

2,8 (22.6) At 9:00. Chisos Formation crops out in foreground. On high skyline, Pummel Peak on the left is on the northeast edge of the Pine Canyon volcano. To right of that peak, Wright and Panther Peaks are on the north edge. Between those peaks and the Park Headquarters in the lower hills is the separate Panther laccolith.

3.2 (22.1) Basin Junction. Park Route 4 is logged separately.

3.4 (21.9) Road to north is the Grapevine Hills Road. It is 7.7 miles to a campsite and trailhead at a reliable spring. Fascinating rock formations and an ideal spot to camp and watch wildlife at the watering hole.

3.5 (21.8) Crossing north edge of Government Spring laccolith intruded into Chisos Formation (BB Figure 17).

5.2 (21.2) Top of Todd Hill. To the north the Rosillos Mountains are an eroded large olivine granite laccolith.

5.8 (19.6) Riding on gravel-covered pediment. Road to north to Paint Gap Hills, a long northeast trending sill. The area is notable for the variety of colors seen along Tornillo Creek near the end of the road. Part of the road requires high-clearance vehicles. There are three campsites accessible by car.

9.4 (16.0) At 9:00 (front of vehicle is 12:00), basal black ledge is Ash Spring Basalt of the Chisos Formation. The basalt contains large feldspar crystals.

9.7 (15.8) Upper Cretaceous Aguja Formation in road cut to right. Fossils in this marine formation include shark teeth, fish vertebrae and poorly preserved casts of clams, oysters and ammonites.

10.0 (15.4) At 3:00, Croton Mountain (elevation 4,800 feet) is a fine-grained granitic intrusion and possible source of the Paint Gap Hills sill.

10.3   (15.1) Road crosses dike in the Upper Cretaceous Aguja Formation. The dike can be traced northwest for three miles.

11.2   (14.2) Upper Cretaceous Aguja Formation.

13.1   (12.3) Ross Maxwell Drive (Park Route 5) junction.

14.6   (10.8) Crossing Burro Mesa Fault. The Chisos Formation to the left in Burro Mesa is on the down-dropped side. Total displacement on the Burro Mesa Fault at this point is about 3,000 feet. The Aguja Formation has sills that make brown ledges (with east dip) on the up-thrown side. In the next mile before the curve of the road to the west, please note the north-trending Chisos Pen anticline on the upthrown side of the fault. Light gray Boquillas flaggy limestones are exposed along the crest of the anticline with Pen Formation clays on the east flank.

15.6   (9.8) At 3:00 in the bottom of the valley, vertical layers are sandstones in the Aguja Formation. To the left of the Aguja are younger dark-colored Javelina clay beds on the down-thrown side of the Burro Mesa Fault. To the south the caprock on this end of Burro Mesa is Tule Mountain trachyandesite, which is the upper member of the Chisos Formation.

16.3   (9.1) At 3:00, on the skyline, the Christmas Mountains (elevation 5,735 feet) have a series of sills that intrude Cretaceous rocks. Little Christmas Mountain is the near pinnacle.

17.2   (8.2) At 9:00, Burro Mesa (elevation 4,000 feet). The highest part is capped by Burro Mesa riebeckite rhyolite, the youngest lava flow from the Pine Canyon volcano. This same lava also caps Emory Peak, the highest peak in the Chisos Mountains (BB Figure 7). The section under this lava includes the Wasp Spring flow breccia member of the South Rim Formation and a nearly complete section of the Chisos Formation. The varicolored clays in the lowlands are in the underlying Cretaceous Javelina Formation.

At 6:30, collapsed volcanic vent. Lavas rim three sides but erosion of this side has exposed the intrusive spine in the center.

18.6   (6.8) At 3:00, Dogie Mountain. The Alamo Creek Basalt, basal member of the Chisos Formation, crops out in the arroyo. Undivided lava and sedimentary rocks of the Chisos Formation overlie the basalt.

19.7   (5.7) At 10.00, on skyline, Mule Ears Peaks. At 8:00, a view of the Window in the Chisos Mountains and Casa Grande Peak through the Window.

20.6   (4.8) At 3:00, in arroyo, clays of the Pen Formation in the crest of the Maverick Mountain anticline.

20.8   (4.6) At 3:00, Maverick Mountain is a trachyte intrusion that uplifted part of the pre-existing Maverick anticline (BB Figure 29).

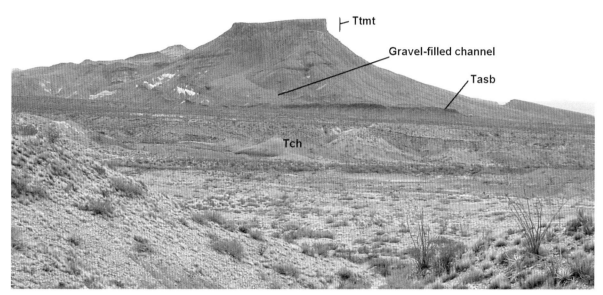

BB Figure 28. View southeast from mile point 21.3 (4.1) of Tule Mountain. Tch=Chisos Formation; Tasb= Ash Spring Basalt; Ttmt= Tule Mountain Trachyandesite, a 200-foot lava bed that caps the mountain.

21.3   (4.1) At 9:00, Tule Mountain (elevation 3,833 feet, BB Figure 28). The slopes below the caprock are composed of about 900 feet of boulder conglomerate that is interpreted as filling of a valley cut into the Chisos section. East of the crest of Tule Mountain there is north-trending fault. Like Burro Mesa, Tule Mountain is an erosional remnant of younger resistant strata on the down-thrown side of the fault.

21.4   (4.0) Maverick Ranger Station. From here to Study Butte the highway is on various Upper Cretaceous Formations.

22.1   (3.3) From here to Study Butte the predominantly shale Upper Cretaceous Javelina, Aguja, and Pen Formations are exposed with essentially no cover.

22.6   (2.8) Cattle guard at entrance to Big Bend National Park. Sill in Javelina Formation on left.

23.8   (1.6) A locality in the Pen Formation about 200 yards to the left is famous for its dwarf invertebrate fauna.

BB Figure 29. Looking northwest at Maverick Mountain, a plug-like mass of trachyte that was intruded into the pre-existing Maverick Anticline an estimated 41 m.y. ago. In the foreground Aguja Formation beds (Kag) dip southwest at about 15 degrees. At the base of the plug Boquillas Limestones (Kbo) are bowed up by the intrusive and have a steep dip of over 35 degrees towards the observer. The black pinnacles are small spine-like intrusives.

24.4   (1.0) Road to Study Butte mercury mine to right. Cinnabar (mercury ore) was mined here until the early 1970's. Ore was found in the intrusive rock and in clay of the Pen Formation.

25.4   (0.0) Junction of State Highways 118 and 170 in Study Butte. Topographic highs to north, east, and west are all igneous plugs intruded into Upper Cretaceous rocks. It is calculated that at the time of intrusion they rose to within 2,000 feet of the surface (Yates and Thompson, 1959). Trans-Pecos Figure 3, with data from Henry and McDowell (1986), shows the ages of these intrusives to range from 47 to 39 m.y.

Chapter 10
Big Bend Ranch State Park
Solitario and the Bofecillos Mountains

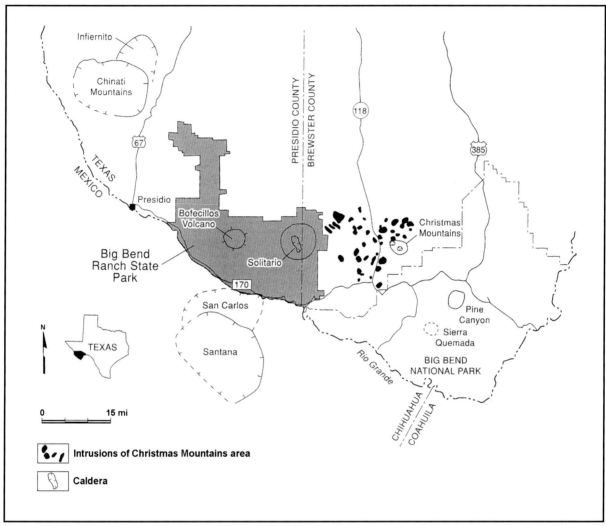

Big Bend Ranch (BBR) Figure 1. Map showing Big Bend Ranch State Park, calderas and other volcanic centers of southern Trans-Pecos Texas and adjacent Chihuahua, Mexico (from Henry, et al, 1998, Figure 2, p.3).

Here is another chance to get off the beaten path and into wild desert scenery with spectacular geology and remote waterfalls. The Big Bend Ranch State Park is in the early stages of development. To get into the state park you have to **pay a fee** at **(1)** Fort Leaton State Historical Park four miles west on Farm to Market Road 170, **(2)** Complex Office in Presidio, or **(3)** go to Warnock Center in Lajitas **and obtain the combination to the entry gate lock**. Plan a minimum of a whole day. Carry all the food, water, and equipment that you might need. The only access into the heart of the park is a well-maintained gravel road. Remember this is a state park. Look, enjoy, photograph, but please don't take samples.

The drive in to the Park Headquarters from the west crosses igneous intrusive and extrusive rocks high on the north flank of the **Bofecillos Mountains**. The mass of the Bofecillos Mountains is the product of **a succession of superimposed volcanoes**, each separated by time and erosion from the succeeding volcano. **Altogether, this succession is the youngest of the volcanic piles of Trans-Pecos.** There are also igneous intrusive features, mainly small laccoliths and many dikes, on either side of the road.

The eastern third of the Park is a laccolith called the **Solitario**. The Solitario is an **extraordinarily large laccolith**. At the present time, access to the Solitario is restricted to hiking or special tours.

Big Bend Ranch State Park is the result of acquisition in 1988 by the state of Texas of a large ranch owned by the Diamond A Cattle Company. The geology of the park is described in recent publications: *Geology of the Solitario Dome, Trans-Pecos, Texas*, Bureau of Economic Geology Report of Investigations No. 240, (C. D. Henry and W.R. Muehlberger, 1996); *Tertiary Volcanism of the Bofecillos Mountains and Big Bend Ranch State Park, Texas,* Bureau of Economic Geology Report of Investigations No. 253 (Henry, et al, 1998); and *Down to Earth at Big Bend Ranch State Park, Texas* (C.D. Henry and J. A. Raney, 2002).

BBR Figure 2. Air photo looking north at the Solitario (Corry, et at, 1990, reproduced with the permission of the Geological Society of America).

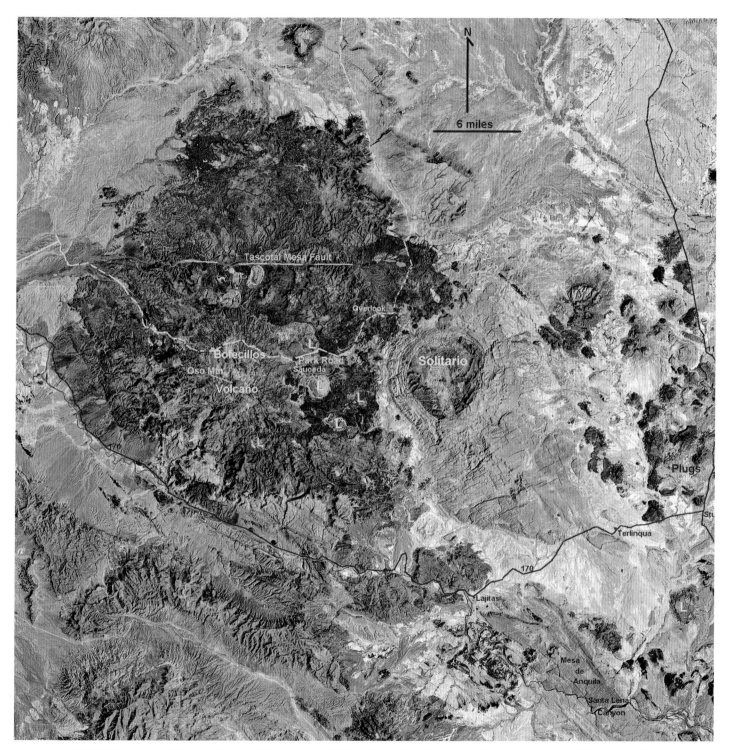

BBR Figure 3. False color satellite image of Big Bend Ranch area. Picture courtesy of Dr. John C. Dohrenwend, Southwest Satellite Imaging, (email: Dohrenwend@rkymtnhi.com). Please note north arrow and scale posted north of the Solitario.

BBR Figure 4. Identification of features of Big Bend Ranch State Park on a satellite image. The domes are small laccoliths. West flowing Teneros Creek is along the Tascotal Mesa Fault (Henry, et al, 1998, Figure 3, p.4)

The Solitario

The **Solitario** is a remarkably circular breached dome on the Presidio-Brewster County line about 10 miles northwest of Terlingua, Texas. The name "El Solitario" derives from early Spanish settlers, who noted the uniqueness of the dome relative to surrounding features and the great difficulty of access. It is a **laccolith more than 10 miles in diameter** that was uplifted by the intrusion at some depth below the surface of a giant lens of igneous rock. This laccolith is much bigger than any other in Texas. Erosion of the crestal rocks has exposed a complete section of Lower Cretaceous rocks on the flanks and provided a window that allows us to study the composition and structures of underlying Paleozoic rocks that normally would be buried thousands of feet below the surface. A small part of the crestal area that collapsed late in the history of igneous activity exposes igneous rocks of the top of the laccolith.

Geologic History

The exposed Paleozoic section begins with Upper Cambrian Dagger Flat Sandstone and continues to the Lower Pennsylvanian with nearly all of the Marathon Uplift (Chapter 2) units represented. The measured thickness of Paleozoic rocks in the Solitario is approximately 8,500 feet (2.6 km) and represents a time span of 240 m.y. Like the sections of the Marathon Uplift the Paleozoic rocks of the Solitario are in the continuation of the Ouachita Trend. They were intensely folded and moved along thrust faults from the southeast to their present position during Late Pennsylvanian to Early Permian time.

As in the Marathon area there is no clear record of sedimentation in the Solitario area from Late Paleozoic to Early Cretaceous time. During the Early Cretaceous a shallow sea flooded this part of Texas and total of 3,900 feet (1.2 km) of carbonates was deposited. These rocks are now exposed for easy study in the shutups (narrow canyons) that cut the rim of the Solitario dome (the name "shutup" derives from the fact that the narrow canyons were easily fenced so that cattle were restricted to the topographically lower crest of the dome).

Near the end of the Cretaceous the Solitario area was uplifted as part of the Tascotal Block. This broad rigid block of the earth's crust was bound on the north by the Tascotal Mesa fault. The block moved eastward during the late stages of the Laramide mountain-building period (please see discussion of anticlines south of Chisos Mountains in the Big Bend Chapter). The west trending trace of the Tascotal Mesa fault north of the Solitario is identified on the satellite image, BBR Figure 3.

The next event evident from the rock record is the series of late Eocene intrusions of igneous rock that formed the laccolith. Intrusive activity in the Solitario occurred in three distinct stages. 1) At 36.0 m.y. numerous sills, dikes and small laccoliths intruded flat-lying Cretaceous rocks and the underlying folded and thrust-faulted Paleozoic rocks. 2) At 35.4 m.y. the main laccolith was formed when magma intruded to form a large lens in Paleozoic rocks at about a 13,000-foot (4-km) depth, possibly along a major thrust fault. Doming uplifted the Paleozoic and Cretaceous rocks and induced radial and concentric faults over the dome. Large-scale ash-flow eruptions from a vent fed by the laccolith led to the creation of a rocks at about a 13,000-foot (4-km) depth, possibly along a major thrust fault. Doming uplifted the Paleozoic and Cretaceous rocks and induced radial and concentric faults over the dome. Large-scale ash-flow eruptions from a vent fed by the laccolith led to the creation of a void in the laccolith and the subsequent collapse of a 3.7 by 1.2-mile (6 x 2-km) caldera in the south-central part of the dome. The caldera was then filled a sequence of breccias, debris-flow deposits, sedimentary rock, and a single trachyte lava. At 35 m.y., numerous dikes and other small intrusions were emplaced into and around the caldera.

Subsequent erosion has created a rim of resistant, tilted Cretaceous limestones that surrounds an interior basin of less-resistant Paleozoic sedimentary and Tertiary igneous rocks (BBR Figure 2). The resulting feature is a striking circular dome 10 miles (16 km) in diameter that is impressive whether viewed from ground, air or satellite.

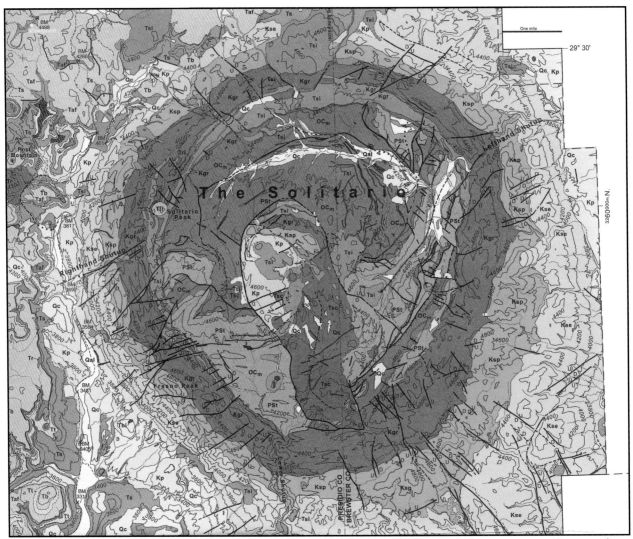

BBR Figure 5. Geologic map of the Solitario (Henry and Raney, 2002). Symbols are same as those used elsewhere in this chapter and the Big Bend Chapter.

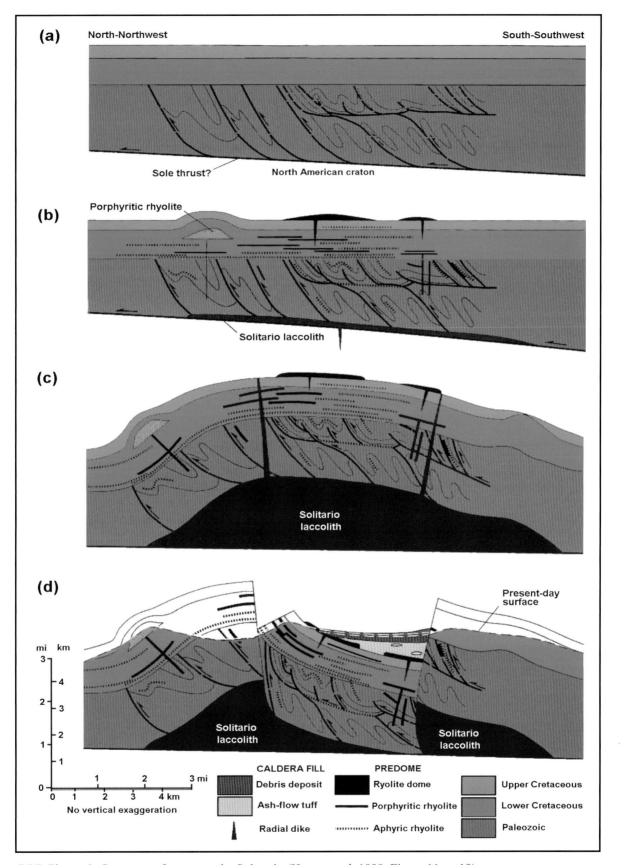

BBR Figure 6. Sequence of events at the Solatario (Henry, et al, 1998, Figure 11, p. 19).

BBR Figure 6. Sequence of events at the Solatario (Henry, et al, 1998, Figure 11, p. 19).

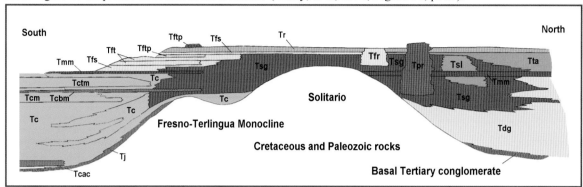

BBR Figure 7. Diagrammatic stratigraphy of Tertiary rocks around the Solitario. On south side Tj=Jeff Conglomerate. **From Big Bend: Tc=Chisos Group, Tcac=Alamo Creek Basalt, Tcbm=Bee Mountain Basalt, Tcm=Mule Ear Spring Tuff, Tctm=Tule Mountain Trachyandesite**. Tsg=Solitario Conglomerate, Tsl=lacustrine limestone of the Solitario Conglomerate, Tdg=Devils Graveyard Formation, Tpr=Terneros Creek Rhyolite, Tmm=Mitchell Mesa Rhyolite, *Tfr, Tfs, Tft, and Tftp=rhyolite lava dome, sedimentary rocks, trachyte, and porphyritic trachyte of the Fresno Formation (respectively, from the early development of the Bofecillos volcano)* Tta=Tascotal Formation, *Tr=Rawls Formation* (from Bofecillos) and Tmb=Basalt of the Closed Canyon Formation (From Henry and Muehlberger, 1996, Figure 48).

Bofecillos Mountains

The **Bofecillos Mountains** are a high plateau **composed almost entirely of lavas and tuffs that erupted from volcanoes within the state park.** Volcanism in the Bofecillos Mountains occurred in several distinct episodes from different sources. Volcanism began about 32.0 m.y. ago with eruption of lavas of the **Fresno Formation. The main period of volcanism is recorded in the Rawls Formation** (27.4-27.2 m.y.). Volcanism continued episodically until about 18.0 m.y. with the eruption of the youngest basalts of the **Closed Canyon Formation** (BBR Table 2 and BBR Figure 8). **Altogether, the Bofecillos volcanics are the youngest of the extrusive rocks of the Trans-Pecos Region.**

The **progression of volcanic events was accompanied by small intrusions** around and in the Bofecillos Mountains in the form of **laccoliths, sills, and dikes**. The laccoliths now form small hills in the eastern half of the park.

The Bofecillos Vent.

Near the middle of the Bofecillo volcano there is a prominent erosional feature called **The Bofecillos Vent**. It consists of a rim of intrusive syenite (26.8 m.y.) surrounding a basin of coarse breccia about one km in diameter. **This vent or at least this area was the eruptive center for a number of ash-flows and lavas of the Rawls Formation.** Rock types in some tuffs indicate the vent area may have collapsed at least twice. The distribution of volcanic rocks in the Rawls Formation indicates that **many of the extrusive rocks came from fissures or local domes across the Bofecillos Mountains.**

The Bofecillos Vent was originally considered the main vent of the Bofecillos Volcano. The coarse breccia of the central basin has clasts (angular pieces of lava) ranging from a few meters to as large as 500 feet (150 m) (please see BBR Figures 13 and 14 and the Oso Loop Road Log). It is similar to the breccias in the Solitario caldera. The breccia is intruded by numerous dikes of quartz trachyte and one basalt dike that is related to the much younger Closed Canyon Formation.

Rocks of the Fresno and Rawls Formation are tilted away from the vent indicating that the vent area was domed sometime after eruption of the Rawls rocks. Doming probably resulted from intrusions in the form of dikes and sills. The outcrop of the coarse intrusive rocks at the top of Oso Mountain and around the vent indicates that a substantial thickness of extrusive rocks must have overlain the area that has been removed by erosion.

BBR Table1. Sources of igneous rocks in Big Bend Ranch State Park.

Formation Age = m.y.	Rocks	Source	Intrusive Structures
Closed Canyon Formation 25-18	Coarse sedimentary Rock, alkali basalt and Rare rhyolitic ash-flow tuff	Basalts are from numerous vents in the State Park	Dikes
Rawls Formation 27.8-27.1	Six volcanic sequences that include basalts, trachyte, quartztrachyte and rhyolite	A complex of volcanoes in the Bofecillos Mountains that together constitute the Bofecillos Volcano	Domes: Leyva, dome west of Sauceda, Solitario Peak intr. Wax Factory, Primero Laccoliths
Santana Tuff 28.8 San Carlos Tuff 30.5	Santana-sparsely Porphyritic welded to non welded rhyolitic tuffs. San Carlos-200 m Welded porphyritic Rhyolite tuff at north edge of caldera	Sierra Rica Caldera Complex of Chihuahua	none
Fresno Formation 32.0-29.2	Rhyolite and basalt lava interbedded with tuffaceous sediments and conglomerate	Fresno Volcano, In southern Bofecillos Mountains	Rhyolitic domes NE Of Sauceo; Llano and Saucedo Trachyte=Racherias Tapada, Javelina, Contabando (gabbroic)
Chisos Group 47-31.8	Tule Mtn. trachyandesite Mule Ear Spring Tuff Bee Mtn, Basalt Alamo Creek Basalt	Sources in Big Bend National Parks and Southwestward in Chihuahua	Solitario 36-35 m.y.

**BBR Table 2. Volcanic Stratigraphy
of the Bofecillos Mountains and Big Bend Ranch State Park**

Formation	Rock Types	Age -in m.y.
Tm **Closed Canyon Formation**	Basalt, conglomerate. minor ash-flow tuff	25-18
Rawls Formation Tra Alazan Lavas Member	Trachyte, porphyritic basalt, basalt	27.23
Trr Rancho Viejo Tuff	Trachyte ash-flow tuff	27.09
Trg Segundo Lavas Member	Quartz trachyte, Porphyritic trachyte	27.06 27.10
Trs Sauceda Lavas Member	Porphyritic basalt, basalt, quartz trachyte,	27.13
Trl Leyva Canyon Member	Quartz trachylte, rhyolite, tuffaceous debris deposits, ash-flow tuff, conglomerate	27.04 27.09 27.33
Trb Las Burras Lavas Member	Basalt	27.5+/-0.2
Ts **Santana Tuff**	Rhyolitic ash-flow tuff	27.79
Tsc **San Carlos Tuff**	Rhyolitic ash-flow tuff	30.50
Fresno Formation Tlb Campo Javelina Basalt Member	Basalt	29.2
Tfpr Peralkaline rhyolite lava	Peralkaline rhyolite lava	30.85
Tftp Rancherias Lvas Member	Trachyte	31.6+/-0.9
Tfr Rhyolitic lava dome	Rhyolite	31.0
Tcs Cienaga Mountain Rhyolite	Rhyolite	32.72
Tmm Mitchell Mesa Rhyolite	Rhyolite ash-flow tuff	32.77
Tm Morita Ranch Formation	Basalt	>32.77
Tpr Terneros Creek Rhyolite	Rhyolite lava domes	35.26-
Chisos Formation Tctm Tule Mtn. Formation	Trachyandesite	31.8
Tcm Mule Ear Spring Tuff	Rhyolitic ash-flow tuff	33.06
Tcbm Bee Mtn. Basalt	Basalt	34.5
Tcac Alamo Creek Basalt	Basalt	47.0

BBR Table 2. Volcanic Stratigraphy from Henry, et al, 1998, Table 1, p.6.

Figure 8 illustrates the manner in which the volcanic pile grew. The Santana Tuff units came from volcanoes to the south in Mexico.

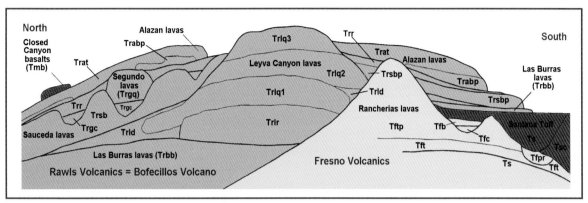

Big Bend Ranch Figure 8. Diagrammatic stratigraphy of Fresno (Tf) and Rawls (Tr) Formations in the Bofecillos Mountains (From Henry, et al, 1998, Figure 5, p.5). Thick lines separate members; thin lines separate individual rock types within member. Santana Tuff (Ts) and San Carlos Tuff (Tsc) are extrusives from volcanoes in Chihuahua. This diagram shows that the Fresno Volcano formed first in the southern part of the volcanic pile and the Rawls period of extrusions was the main contributor to the pile. The Bofecillos Vent is a late feature near the middle of the pile.

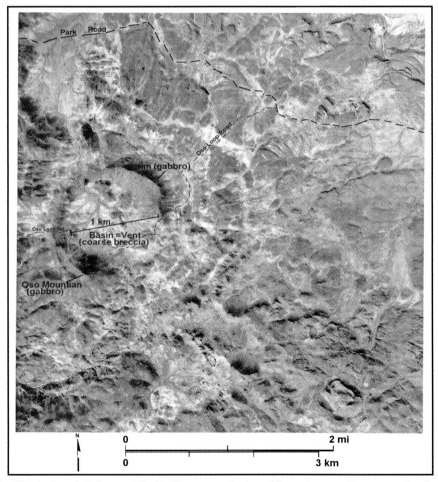

BBR Figure 9. Vertical aerial photo of Bofecillos vent. A rim of intrusive syenite surrounds a basin floored by coarse breccia. The Basin is about 0.6 miles (1 km) in diameter (from Henry, et al, 1998, Figure 18, p.39).

Big Bend Ranch Road Log

This log covers the roads from Farm to Market Road 170 to the Solitario viewpoint northeast of the Sauceda Ranch Park Headquarters. At 8.1 miles from the highway there is a locked gate. **Prior to leaving highway one needs to pay entry fee and get combination to gate lock at one of the following locations: (1) Fort Leaton State Park, 4 miles west of this junction, (2) Complex Office in Presidio, or (3) Warnock Visitor Center in Lajitas.**

Mileage

0.0   Leave Farm to Market Road (FM) 170 and travel northeast on Casa Piedra Road, Ranch to Market (RM) 169. This is a graded road on Late Tertiary and Quaternary gravels.

5.7   Bear right at Y. Road to left goes to Casa Piedra.

6.7   Cross Black Hills Creek.

7.1   Bear left at Y.

8.1   Locked Gate at boundary of Big Bend Ranch. You get the combination when you pay the entry fee.

8.3   Terneros Creek.

9.3   Right at junction.

9.4   Cattle Guard. Scarp to right is capped by basalt porphyry on the upthrown southeast side of the southwest continuation of Tascotal Mesa fault. This fault separates extrusive rocks from gravels on the down-thrown side.

11.5   Road is on northwest flank of Bofecillos Volcano. Lavas overlie volcanic ash beds. There are a number of northwest trending faults in this area.

11.9   Ranch road to right.

12.9   Rancho Viejo Exhibit.

13.2   Entering Bofecillos Canyon.

13.3   Las Cuevas Amarillas Exhibit. In this area, erosion has developed shallow caves in the yellow to white interval that consists of volcanic tuff (ash) and debris flows (coarser material that was saturated by water to a slurry and transported by gravity (Leyva Canyon Member of Rawls Formation). The white-yellow beds are overlain by dark porphyritic basalts lavas (Sauceda Lavas Member of Rawls Formation). Look for an overhang at right side of the road that was used by Indians as a shelter. A short walk will find pictographs, metates, and smoke stains. Please do not disturb the artifacts.

15.3   Bofecillos Creek with cottonwoods to left. To the right about 500 yards there is a small laccolith intruded into a yellow ash-flow tuff of the Rawls Formation.

BBR Figure 10. White to yellow ash beds of the Cuevas Amarillas area are overlain by basalt lavas.

17.3   Cattle guard. Oso Peak at 1.00 is a gabbro intrusive on the south side of the Bofecillos Vent. Following this road log, the Oso Loop Road Log covers a trip through the vent.

17.9   Water in the Desert Exhibit. Ojito Adentro (Little Spring) is in the thick cottonwood grove (BBR Figure 11). The cliff above the cottonwood grove is quartz trachyte lava. Trail is a 1.4 mile (2 km) round trip.

18.2   Oso Peak at 1.00. Quartz trachyte lava on left.

18.6   Exhibit

19.0   Cattle guard. Lavas on left.

19.4   Brick red outcrops in this area are baked soils below lavas.

19.8   Large corral. The west end of Oso Loop is at east side of corrals.

21.3   Exhibit.

21.6   Cattle guard.

21.8   Papalotito Colorado camping area is about ½ mile to left

BBR Figure 11. View at MP 17.9 to the north of Ojito Adrento from roadside exhibit.

23.9   East end of Oso Loop.

24.0   Cattle guard. Several small dikes in this area.

25.0   Cinco Tinajas. There are five ponds along Leyva canyon to the north. Trail is a 0.9-mile (1.5 km) loop.

26.1   Sauceda. Park visitor center is at east end of metal building east of ranch house. Accommodations here include three rooms in the Big House and bunks in the Lodge. Reservations: (432) 229-3416 or /www.tpwd.state.tx.us. Continue east, north of the Big House.

26.9   Lava flow. Silicic trachyte lava in the Fresno Formation. Road is on the south flank of a small laccolith.

27.1   Leyva campground road.

27.7   Cattle guard. Solitario at 2.00.

28.2   East end of Llano Loop road.

29.6   La Posta camp ground to right.

30.5   Exhibit. The Plateau Grasslands.

BBR Figure 12. View of Cretaceous rocks of west flank from Solitario viewpoint. The west-dipping rocks on this side of the laccolith are slabs of massive Lower Cretaceous limestones.

32.9   Solitario Viewpoint (of southwest flank of Solitario). The Solitario is a feature of great interest in the Park, but it is not open for easy visit. Beyond this point, the road is not maintained and a high clearance vehicle is needed. In addition, to get into the Solitario you have to arrange in advance ([432] 229-3416) to take a conducted tour from the visitor's center. Hopefully, in the future the Park Service will improve the road so that all can visit the interior of the Solitario.

33.8   Pila Montoya. Road to right goes to Solitario. Road to left connects with county road to Wire Gap and Marfa.

The continuation of this log into the east part of the Solitario Basin (Tres Papalotes) can be found in Pause and Spears, 1986, p. 15, starting at mile point 77.5.

Oso Loop Road Log

The road traverses the upper flanks of the Bofecillos Volcano and the Bofecillos Vent from east to west (BBR Figure 9). This is a rough road for high clearance vehicles only. Fortunately the road is open to all.

<u>Mileage</u>
0.0   East end of road 2.2 miles west of Sauceda ranch house. Road is on silicic trachyte lava.

1.7   Y-bear right. Roadbed is on syenite lava on east side of Bofecillos vent.

1.9   Entering vent (BBR Figures 14 and 15).

2.0   Y-bear right.

2.1   Pila de Oso tank (water hole or trough for cattle).

2.8   Stone lined tanks.

3.1   Gate (elevation about 4,550 ft) on west side of vent. Oso Mountain (elevation 5,135 ft) to south is the highest point in Big Bend Ranch State Park.

3.4   Tank.

3.6   White rhyolite lava.

3.9   Purple basalt dike.

4.3   Y bear right.

4.4   Tank.

5.1   Campo de la Vibora.

5.6   Two small dikes on left.

5.8   Corral gate.

5.9   Main road and west end of Oso Loop.

Right to Park Headquarters, left to exit park.

BBR Figure 13. Cactus on weathered porphyritic lava along Farm to Market Road 170.

BBR Figure 14.   View to northwest across vent.   Intrusive rocks that resist erosion core the hills in the background. Dark mounds in foreground are quartz trachyte lava that was intruded into the breccia in the vent.

BBR Figure 15. Outcrop of breccia in vent. A deep pit or hole was formed by either collapse or a large explosion of the volcano. This hole was then filled by angular pieces of lava that fell back into the vent or flowed in from the sides. The width of the larger pieces is two inches (5 cm).

BBR Figure 16. Outcrops north of FM 170 of Rawls Formation volcanics on southwest flank of the volcano.

References Cited

General References

Bureau of Economic Geology, 1992, Geologic Map of Texas.

Bureau of Economic Geology, 1996, Physiographic Map of Texas.

Bureau of Economic Geology, 1997, Tectonic Map of Texas.

Denison, R. E. and E. A. Hetherington, Jr., 1969, Basement Rocks in far west Texas and south-central New Mexico: *in* Kottlowski, F. E. and D. V. Malone, *editors*, Border Stratigraphic Symposium, New Mexico Institute of Mining and Technology Circular 104.

Hills, J.M., 1985, Structural Evolution of the Permian Basin of West Texas and New Mexico: in Structure and Tectonics of Trans-Pecos, Texas, P.W. Dickerson and W. R. Muehlberger, editors, WTGS Field Conference Guidebook 85-81, p. 89-99.

Jackson, J.A., 1997, Glossary of Geology, Fourth Edition: American Geological Institute, Alexandria, Virginia.

King, P. B., 1965, Geology of the Sierra Diablo Region Texas: U. S. Geological Survey Prof. Paper 480.

King, P. B. and P. T. Flawn, 1953, Geology and Mineral Deposits of Pre-Cambrian Rocks of the Van Horn Area, Texas: The Univ. of Texas Publication No. 5301

King, P. B., 1965, Geology of the Sierra Diablo Region Texas: U. S. Geological Survey Prof. Paper 480.

King, P. B. and P. T. Flawn, 1953, Geology and Mineral Deposits of Pre-Cambrian Rocks of the Van Horn Area, Texas: The Univ. of Texas Publication No. 5301

Leaf, Gary, 2001, Precambrian Rocks of the Van Horn Region, West Texas: Structure and Stratigraphy: Abstract in West Texas Geol. Soc. Bull. V. 40, No. 6, p.25.

McGookey, D. P., 1975, Gulf Coast Cenozoic sediments and structure: An excellent example of extra-continental sedimentation: Transactions – Gulf Coast Assoc. of Geological Societies, V. 25, p. 104-120.

Muehlberger, W.R., 1992, Tectonic Map of North America: American Assoc. of Petroleum Geologists.

Reynolds, David, 1985, Deformation along the Late Precambrian Steeruwitz Thrust   near Allamore, Hudspeth County, Texas: *in* Dickerson, P.W. and W. R. Muehlberger, *Ed.*,

Structure and Tectonics of Trans-Pecos, Texas, West Texas Geological Society Field Conf Guide Book 85-81, p. 107-115.

Spearing, Darwin, 1991, Roadside Geology of Texas: Mountain Press Publishing Company, Box 2399, Missoula, Montana 59806.

Chapter 2
Ouachita-Marathon Trend

Dickinson, W.R. and T.F. Lawton, 2003, Sequential intercontinental suturing as the ultimate control for Pennsylvanian Ancestral Rocky Mountains deformation: Geol. Soc. America Geology v.31, p. 609-612.

Flawn, P.T., A. Goldstein, Jr.,P. B. King and C. E. Weaver, 1961, The Ouachita System: The Univ. of Texas , Bur. of Economic Geology Publ. No. 6120 (3rd Printing, March, 1980).

King, P. B., 1937, Geology of the Marathon Region, Texas: U. S. Geological Survey Prof. Paper 187.

Denison, R. E. and E. A. Hetherington, Jr., 1969, Basement Rocks in far west Texas and south-central New Mexico: *in* Kottlowski, F. E. and D. V. Malone, *editors*, Border Stratigraphic Symposium, New Mexico Institute of Mining and Technology Circular 104.

Laroche, T.M. and J.J. Viveiros, *editors*, 1994, Structure and tectonics of the Big Bend area and southern Permian Basin, Texas: West Texas Guidebook, Publ. 94-95

Leaf, Gary, 2001, Precambrian Rocks of the Van Horn Region, West Texas: Structure and Stratigraphy: Abstract in West Texas Geol. Soc. Bull. V. 40, No. 6, p.25.
King, P. B., 1965, Geology of the Sierra Diablo Region Texas: U. S. Geological Survey Prof. Paper 480.

King, P. B. and P. T. Flawn, 1953, Geology and Mineral Deposits of Pre-Cambrian Rocks of the Van Horn Area, Texas: The Univ. of Texas Publication No. 5301
Maxwell, R. A. J. T. Lonsdale, R. T. Hazzard and J. A. Wilson, 1967, Geology of Big Bend National Park, Brewster County, Texas: Univ. of Texas Bureau of Economic Geology Publ. No. 6711.

Muehlberger, W. R., DeMis, W. D. and J. O. Leason, 1984, Geologic Map and Cross Sections, Marathon Region, Trans-Pecos, Texas: Geol Soc. Of America Map and Chart Series MC 28-T, Scale: 1:250,000.

Muehlberger, W.R., C. Chandler and Ed Dickerson, 1985, Road Log from Alpine to Marathon Fold Belt and Return to Midland: in Structure and Tectonics of Trans-Pecos,

Texas, P.W. Dickerson and W. R. Muehlberger, *editors*, West Texas Geological Society Field Conference Guidebook 85-81, page 28.

Reynolds, David, 1985, Deformation along the Late Precambrian Steeruwitz Thrust   near Allamore, Hudspeth County, Texas: *in* Dickerson, P.W. and W. R. Muehlberger, *Ed.*, Structure and Tectonics of Trans-Pecos, Texas, West Texas Geological Society Field Conf Guide Book 85-81, p. 107-115.

Ross, C.A. and J. R. Ross, 1985, Paleozoic Tectonics and Sedimentation in West texas, Southern New Mexico and Southern Arizona: *in* Structure and Tectonics of Trans-Pecos, Texas, P.W. Dickerson and W. R. Muehlberger, *editors*, West Texas Geological Society Field Conference Guidebook 85-81, p.221-230.

Viele, G. W., 1979, Geologic Map and Cross Section, Eastern Ouachita Mountains, Arkansas: Map Summary: Geol. Soc. America Bull. V. 90, P1096-1099.

Chapter 3
Llano Uplift

Barnes, V. E., et al, 1972, Geology of the Llano Region and Austin Area: Field Excursion, Bur. Economic Geology Guidebook Number 13.

Denison, R. E. and E. A. Hetherington, Jr., 1969, Basement Rocks in far west Texas and south-central New Mexico: *in* Kottlowski, F. E. and D. V. Malone, *editors*, Border Stratigraphic Symposium, New Mexico Institute of Mining and Technology Circular 104. Geologic Atlas of Texas Brownwood Sheet, 1976, Bureau of Economic Geology.

Dickinson, W.R. and T.F. Lawton, 2003, Sequential intercontinental suturing as the ultimate control for Pennsylvanian Ancestral Rocky Mountains deformation: Geol. Soc. America Geology v.31, p. 609-612.

Jensen, J.G., 1980, Precambrian geology of the Llano Region, Central Texas: *in* Windle, Del, *editor*, Geology of the Llano Region, Central Texas: West Texas Geological Society Guidebook, Publ. 80-73.

Llano Sheet , Geologic Atlas of Texas, 1981, Bureau of Economic Geology.

Loewy, Staci, 2003, Recreating Ancient Geological Puzzle involving Texas: Focus on Science, Winter , 2003, Published by the College of Natural Sciences at the University of Texas at Austin.

Leaf, Gary, 2001, Precambrian Rocks of the Van Horn Region, West Texas: Structure and Stratigraphy: Abstract in West Texas Geological Society Bull. V. 40, No. 6, p.25.

McBride, E.F., A. Abdel-Wahab and K.L. Milliken, 2002. Petrography and Diagenesis of a Half-Billion Year-Old Cratonic Sandstone (Hickory), Llano Region, Texas: Bureau of Economic Geology Rept of Investigations No. 264

Simpson, B. W., 1958, Gem Trails of Texas: Newman Stationary and Printing Co., Dallas, Texas.

Windle, Del, 1980, *editor*, Geology of the Llano Region, Central Texas: West Texas Geological Society Guidebook, Publ. 80-73.

Chapter 4
Permian Basin

Bebout, D. G. and K. J. Meador, 1985, Regional Cross sections Central Basin Platform, West Texas: Bureau of Economic Geology.

Bebout, D.G. and Charles Kerans, 1993, Guide to the Permian Reef Geology Trail, McKittrick Canyon, Guadalupe Mountains National Park, West Texas: Bureau of Economic Geology Guidebook 26.

Brown, L. F., R.F.S Iriarte and D. A. Jones, 1987, Regional Stratigraphic Cross Sections, Upper Pennsylvanian and Lower Permian Strata (Virgilian and Wolfcampian Series), North-Central Texas: Bureau of Economic Geology.

Dickinson, W.R. and T.F. Lawton, 2003, Sequential intercontinental suturing as the ultimate control for Pennsylvanian Ancestral Rocky Mountains deformation: Geol. Soc. America Geology v.31, p. 609-612.

Frenzel, H.N. and others,1988, The Permian Basin Region: *in* GSA DNAG The Geology of North America Volume D-2, p.261-306.

Galloway, W.E. T.E. Ewing, C.M Garrett, N. Tyler and D.G. Bebout, 1983, Atlas of Major Texas Oil Reservoirs: Bureau of Economic Geology.

Hanson, B. M and others, 1991, The Permian Basin: *in* Economic Geology, U.S., Geol. Soc. America DNAG v. P-2, p.339-356.

Hill, C.A., 1990, Sulfuric acid speleogenesis of Carlsbad Cavern and its relationship to hydrocarbons, Delaware Basin, New Mexico and Texas: Amer. Assoc. Petroleum Geologists Bull. v.74, p.1685-1694.

Hill, C. A., 1996, Geology of the Delaware Basin Guadalupe, Apache and Glass Mountains, New Mexico and West Texas: Permian Basin Section-SEPM Publ. No. 96-39.

Hills, J.M., 1972, Late Paleozoic Sedimentation in West Texas Permian Basin: Amer. Assoc. Petroleum Geologists Bull. v.56, p.2303-2322.

Hills, J.M., 1985, Structural Evolution of the Permian Basin of West Texas and New Mexico: in Structure and Tectonics of Trans-Pecos, Texas, P.W. Dickerson and W. R. Muehlberger, editors, WTGS Field Conference Guidebook 85-81, p. 89-99.

Jones, T.S., Chairman, Stratigraphic Problems Committee, 1949, East-West Cross Section through Permian Basin of West Texas: West Texas Geological Society.

King, P.B., 1948, Geology of the Southern Guadalupe Mountains: U.S. Geological Survey Prof. Paper 215.

Mazullo, S. J., 1982,Stratigraphy and depositional mosaics of Lower Clearfork and Wichita Groups (Permian): Amer. Assoc. Petroleum Geologists Bull. v.66, p.210-227.

Ramondetta, P.J., 1982, Genesis and emplacement of oil in the San Andres Formation, Northern Shelf of the Midland Basin, Texas: Texas Bureau of Economic Geology Report of Investigations No. 116.

Silver, B.A. and R.G. Todd, 1969, Permian Cyclic Strata, Northern Midland and Delaware Basins, West Texas and southeast New Mexico: Amer. Assoc. Petroleum Geologists Bull. v.53, p.2223-2251.

Todd, R.G., 1976, Oolite-bar progradation, San Andres Formation, Midland Basin, Texas: Amer. Assoc. Petroleum Geologists Bull. v.60, p.907-925.

Vest, E. L., Jr., 1970, Oil fields of Pennsylvanian-Permian Horseshoe Atoll: *in* Halbouty, M.T., *editor*, Geology of Giant Oil Fields, Amer. Assoc. Petroleum Geologists Memoir 14, p.185-203.

Wilde, G.L. and R.G. Todd, 1968, Guadalupian Biostratigraphic Relationships and sedimentation in the Apache Mountains Region, West Texas: Permian Basin Section SEPM 1968 Guidebook, p.10-31.

Wright, W.F., 1979, Petroleum Geology of the Permian Basin: West Texas Geological Society 79-71.

Permian Reefs

Hill, C. A., 1990, Sulfuric acid speleogenesis of Carlsbad Cavern and other caves in the Guadalupe Mountains, New Mexico and Texas: Amer. Assoc. Petroleum Geologists Bull. v.74, p1685-1694.

King, P.B., Guadalupe Mountains: U.S. Geological Survey Prof. Paper 215

Wood, J. W., 1968, Geology of Apache Mountains, Trans-Pecos, Texas: Bureau of Economic Geology Geologic Quad. Map no. 35.

Chapter 5
Sierra Madera Astroblem

Bureau of Economic Geology, Geologic Atlas of Texas, Fort Stockton Sheet, 1994.

Howard, K. A., T.W. Offield and H. G. Wilshire, 1972, Structure of Sierra Madera, Texas, as a Guide to Central Peaks of Lunar Crates: Geological Society of America Bull. v.83, p 2795-2808.

King, P. B., 1930, The Geology of the Glass Mountains, Texas, Part 1, Descriptive Geology: Texas Univ. Bull. 3038. 167 p.

Naldreff, A.J., 2003, From Impact to Riches: Evolution of Geological Understanding as Seen at Sudbury, Canada: Geological Society of America Today, v. 13, no.2, p.4-9.

Wilshire, H.G., T. W. Offield, K. A. Howard, and David Cummings, 1972, Geology of the Sierra Madera Cryptoexplosion Structure, Pecos County, Texas: U.S. Geol. Survey Prof. Paper 599-H

Chapter 6
Llano Estacado

Cronin, J. G., 1964, A Summary of the occurrence and development of ground water in the Southern High Plains of Texas: U. S. Geol Survey Water-Supply Paper 1683, 88 p.

Frye, J. C. and A. B. Leonard, 1957 , Relation of Ogallala Formati0on to the Southern High Plains in Texas: Texas Bureau of Economic Geology Report of Investigations No. 51.

Frye, J. C., 1970, The Ogallala Formation - a review: Ogallala Aquifer Symposium, Texas Tech Univ. Special Report No. 39, p.5-14. (Rayner p.11-117)

Gustavson, T. C., 1996, Fluvial and Eolian Depositional Systems, Paleosols, and Paleoclimate of the Upper Cenozoic Ogallala and Blackwater Draw Formations, Southern

High Plains, Texas and New Mexico: Texas Bureau of Economic Geology Report of Investigations No. 239.

Hovorka, S. D., 1995, Quaternary Evolution of Playa Lakes of the Southern High Plains-A Case Study from the Amarillo Area, Texas: Texas Bureau of Economic Geology Report of Investigations No. 236.

Mullican, W. F. III, N.D.. Johns and A.E. Fryar, 1997, Playas and Recharge of the Ogallala Aquifer in the Southern High Plains of Texas-An Examination Using Numerical Techniques: Texas Bureau of Economic Geology Report of Investigations No. 242.

Nativ, Ronit, 1988, Hydrogeology and Hydrochemistry of the Ogallala Aquifer, Southern High Plains, Texas Panhandle and Eastern New Mexico: Texas Bureau of Economic Geology Report of Investigations No. 177.

Paine, J. G. 1995, Shallow-Seismic Evidence for Playa Basin development by Dissolution-Induced Subsidence in the Southern High Plains, Texas: Texas Bureau of Economic Geology Report of Investigations No. 233.

Reeves, C. C., Jr., 1972, Tertiary-Quaternary stratigraphy and geomorphology of West Texas and south-eastern New Mexico: *in* Kelley, V. C. and F. D. Trauger, *editors*, Guidebook of East-Central New Mexico: New Mexico Geol Soc 23rd Field Conf., p. 108-117.

Seni, S. J., 1980, Sand-body Geometry and Depositional Systems, Ogallala Formation, Texas: Texas Bureau of Economic Geology Report of Investigations No. 105

Chapter 7
Tertiary Volcanism across the
Trans-Pecos Region of West Texas

Henry, C. D. and F.W. McDowell, 1986, Geochronology of magmatism in the Tertiary volcanic field, Trans-Pecos Texas: *in* Price, J.G., C.D. Henry, D.F. Parker and D.S. Barker, Igneous Geology of Trans-Pecos Texas, Bureau of Economic Geology Guidebook 23, p.99-122.

Maxwell, R.A., 1979, The Big Bend of the Rio Grande: Bureau of Economic Geology Guidebook 7.

Price, J.G., C.D. Henry, D.F. Parker and D.S. Barker, *editors*, Igneous Geology of Trans-Pecos Texas, Bureau of Economic Geology Guidebook 23, p.99-122.

Walton, A.W., and C. D. Henry, *editors*, Cenozoic Geology of the Trans-Pecos Volcanic Field of Texas: Bureau of Economic Geology Guidebook 19, p.97-105.

Chapter 8
Davis Mountains

Anderson, J. E., Jr., 1968, Igneous Geology of the Central Davis Mountains, Jeff Davis County, Texas: Bureau of Economic Geology Geologic Quad. Map no. 36.

Henry, C. D., M. E. Kunk and W.C. McIntosh. 1994, 40Ar/39Ar chronology and volcanology of salicic volcanism in the Davis Mountains, Trans-Pecos, Texas: Geol. Soc. America Bull. v.106, p.1359-1376.

Henry, C. D. and F.W. McDowell, 1986, Geochronology of magmatism in the Tertiary volcanic field, Trans-Pecos Texas: *in* Price, J.G., C.D. Henry, D.F. Parker and D.S. Barker, Igneous Geology of Trans-Pecos Texas, Bureau of Economic Geology Guidebook 23, p.99-122.

Mattison, G.D., 1979, A Reinterpretation of the Sheep Pasture Tuffs (Mount Locke): *in* Cenozoic Geology of the Trans-Pecos Volcanic Field of Texas: *in* A. W. Walton and C. D. Henry, *editors*, Bureau of Economic Geology Guidebook 19, p. 83-91.

Parker, D. F., 1979, The Paisano Volcano: Stratigraphy, Age, and Petrogenesis: *in* Cenozoic Geology of the Trans-Pecos Volcanic Field of Texas: *in* A. W. Walton and C. D. Henry, *editors*, Bureau of Economic Geology Guidebook 19, p.97-105.

Parker, D.F., 1983, Origin of the trachyte-quartz trachyte-peralkalic rhyolite suite of the Oligocene Paisano VolcanoTrans-Pecos, Texas: Geol. Soc. America Bull. v.94, p.614-629.

Parker, D.F., J. G. Price and C.D. Henry, 1986, Road Log Day 2 – Van Horn toAlpine: *in* Price, J.G., C.D. Henry, D.F. Parker and D.S. Barker, *editors*, Igneous Geology of Trans-Pecos Texas, Bureau of Economic Geology Guidebook 23, fig. 53, p.71.

Stevens, J. B., 1979, Eocene-Oligocene Volcaniclastic Sediments, West-Central Brewster County and adjacent Presidio County, Trans-Pecos, Texas: *in* Cenozoic Geology of the Trans-Pecos Volcanic Field of Texas: A. W. Walton and C. D. Henry, *editors*, Bureau of Economic Geology Guidebook 19, p.150-156.

Von Steeruwitz, W. H., 1979, Memorial Edition, Geologic Atlas of Texas, 1979, Marfa Sheet: Bureau of Economic Geology.

Von Steeruwitz, W. H., 1995, Fort Stockton Sheet: Geologic Atlas of Texas, Bureau of Economic Geology.

Chapter 9
Big Bend

Ben-Avaham, Zvi and Susan Hough, 2003, Promised Land: Natural History, Vol. 112, No. 9 (Oct. 2003), p. 44-49.

Big Bend Natural History Association, 1993, Road Guide to backcountry dirt roads of Big Bend National Park

Big Bend Natural History Association, 1999, Road Guide to paved and improved roads of Big Bend National Park.

Bolden, G.P., R.B. Harrington and W.J. Traeder, editors,1972 (reprint of 1965 Guidebook with additions), Geology of the Big Bend Area, Texas: West Texas Geological Society Publication 72-59.

Daily, Michael, Age relations in alkaline rocks from the Big Bend region, Texas: *in* Cenozoic Geology of the Trans-Pecos Volcanic Field of Texas: A. W. Walton and C. D. Henry, *editors*, Bureau of Economic Geology Guidebook 19, p.92-96.

Geologic Atlas of Texas Emory Peak-Presidio Sheet: Texas Bureau of Economic Geology

Harlan, S.S., J.W. Geissman, C.D. Henry and T.C. Onstott, 1995, Paleomagnetism and 40Ar/39Ar geochronology of gabbro sills at Mariscal Mountain Anticline, southern Big Bend National Park, Texas: Implications for the timing of Laramide tectonism and vertical axis rotations in the Southern Cordilleran orogenic belt: Tectonics, v.14, no.2, p.307-321.

Indest, Stanley and Max Carman, 1979, Crystallization History of the Wildhorse Mountain Quartz Syenite Intrusion and it s relation to some other Big Bend Intrusions (Study Butte are plugs): *in* A. W. Walton and C. D. Henry, *editors*, Bureau of Economic Geology Guidebook 19, p.72-82.

Laroche, T. M. and J.J. Vivieros, *editors*, 1994, Structure and tectonics of the Big Bend and southern Permian Basin, Texas: West Texas Geological Society Guidebook 94-95.

Maxwell, R.S., J.T. Lonsdale, R.T. Hazzard and J. A. Wilson, 1967, Geology of Big Bend National Park, Brewster County, Texas: Univ. Texas Publ. No. 6711 (Bureau of Economic Geology).

Maxwell, R.A., 1979, The Big Bend of the Rio Grande: Bureau of Economic Geology Guidebook 7.

Maxwell, R.A. and J.W. Dietrich, 1972, Geology of the Big Bend Area, Texas: West Texas Geological Society Publication 72-59.

Metcalfe, C.W. and A.C. Clark, 1979, Gravity measurements in the Big Bend as part of a continental rift: *in* Cenozoic Geology of the Trans-Pecos Volcanic Field of Texas, A. W. Walton and C. D. Henry, *editors*, Bureau of Economic Geology Guidebook 19 p.33-38.

McDowell, F.W., 1979, Potassium-argon dating in the Trans-Pecos Texas volcanic field: *in* Cenozoic Geology of the Trans-Pecos Volcanic Field of Texas, A. W. Walton and C. D. Henry, *editors*, Bureau of Economic Geology Guidebook 19 p.67-70.

Ogley, D.S., 1979, Eruptive History of the Pine Canyon Caldera, (northeastern half of Chisos Mountains) Big Bend Park: *in* Cenozoic Geology of the Trans-Pecos Volcanic Field of Texas, A. W. Walton and C. D. Henry, *editors*, Bureau of Economic Geology Guidebook 19 p.67-70.

Pause, P.H. and R.G. Spears, *editors*, 1986, Geology of the Big Bend Area and Solitario Dome: West Texas Geological Society Guidebook 86-82.

Yates, R.G., and G.A. Thompson, 1959, Geology and Quicksilver Deposits of the Terlingua District, Texas: U. S. Geological Survey Professional Paper 312.

Chapter 10
Big Bend Ranch State Park

Corry, C., E., E. Herrin, F.W. McDowell and K.A. Phillips, 1990, Geology of the Solitario, Trans-Pecos, Texas: Geol. Soc. America Special Paper 250.

Geologic Atlas of Texas Emory Peak-Presidio Sheet: Texas Bureau of Economic Geology.

Henry, C.D. and W.R. Muehlberger, 1996, Geology of the Solitario dome, Trans-Pecos, Texas, Bureau of Economic Geology Report of Investigations No.240.

Henry, C. D., L.L. Davis, M.J. Kunk and W,C. McIntosh, 1998, Tertiary Volcanism of the Bofecillos Mountains and Big Bend Ranch State Park, Texas: Bureau of Economic Geology Rept. of Investigations No. 253.

Henry, C.D. and J. A. Raney, 2002, Down to earth at Big Bend Ranch State Park, Texas (Geologic Map and Trail-side Geology): Bureau of Economic Geology

McKnight, J. F., 1970, Geology of the Bofecillos Mountains Area, Trans-Pecos, Texas: Bureau of Economic Geology Geologic Quadrangle Map 37.

Pause, P.H. and R.G. Spears, *editors*, 1986, Geology of the Big Bend Area and Solitario Dome: West Texas Geological Society Guidebook 86-82.

Wilson, J.A., J.B. Stevens and M. S. Stevens, 1979, New Cross Sections from Southern Davis Mountains to Northeast Solitario: *in* Cenozoic Geology of the Trans-Pecos Volcanic

Field of Texas: A. W. Walton and C. D. Henry, *editors*, Bureau of Economic Geology Guidebook 19, p. 147-149.

Yates, R.G., and G.A. Thompson, 1959, Geology and Quicksilver Deposits of the Terlingua District, Texas: U. S. Geological Survey Professional Paper 312.

Big Bend. Hoar frost along Basin Drive north of Panther Pass, February 2004.

Glossary of Geologic Terms

Allochthonous Layers of rocks that have been transported horizontally long distances (sometimes tens of miles) by overthrust faulting.

Alluvium Unconsolidated sand and mud deposited by streams or wind..

Andesite See *Igneous Rocks*

Anticline Where rock layers (beds) are arched up (up-folded) so the beds on the two sides of the fold are inclined (dip) away from each other along a common ridge or axis, similar to the two opposite slopes in the roof of a quonset hut. Opposite of *Syncline*, which is a down fold of bedded rocks.

Anticlinorium a series of parallel anticlines that have an overall arch shape.

Arkose Sandstone with a high percentage of feldspar grains.

Ash flow An avalanche of volcanic ash. Generally a highly heated mixture of volcanic gases and ash that flows down the flanks of a volcano.

Ash-flow tuff Consolidated volcanic ash that was originally deposited by an ash flow.

Batholith A large irregular mass of intrusive igneous rock underlying or exposed over an area greater than 100 km^2. Batholiths originate as deep seated igneous rock masses (harden magma).

Bedding A characteristic of sedimentary rocks in which parallel planar surfaces separate layers of different grain sizes or composition deposited at different times.

Breached Erosion has removed strata over the crestal part of a dome or anticline to expose older rocks in the core.

Breccia A fragmental rock whose component particles are angular, thus distinguished from a conglomerate, which is composed of rounded pebbles, cobbles or boulders. Can include pebble to bounder-size angular rocks.

b.y. or Ga Billions of years before present.

Caldera A large basin-shaped volcanic depression that forms after a very large eruption when the volcano collapses through the roof of the emptied magma chamber.

Carbonate   Includes limestones and dolomites. Rocks that have CO_3 in their chemical formula.

Center (volcanic) Source area of an extrusive volcanic pile. May include one or many vents.

Central vent   The main vent of a volcano, situated at the center of the cone.

Cenozoic   Geologic era from 65 m.y. to Present. Periods are:

Period	Begins
Quaternary	1.8 m.y.
Tertiary	65 m.y.

Clastic   Includes all rocks that are made up of particles of other rocks, e.g.. conglomerates, sandstones, siltstones and shales.

Cyclothem, cyclothemic deposition During the Late Paleozoic changes of sea level caused by periodic development of continental glaciers in the southern hemisphere result in low sea levels during glacial periods and high in-between. This resulted in the deposition of carbonate sediments during high stands and clastic sediments during low stands.

Diatreme   A volcanic vent filled with volcanic breccia. Formed by the explosive escape of gases.

Dike   A tabular igneous intrusion that cuts across structures of surrounding rock.

Dip   The angle by which bedding of sedimentary or extrusive rocks deviates from the horizontal. The angle is measured in a plane perpendicular to the *strike*.

Dolomite and dolomitization Under semi-evaporitic conditions dolomite is deposited instead of limestone. Dolomite has magnesium plus calcium in a chemical formula $CaMg\ CO_3$. Limestone is also changed to dolomite where a reflux action (essentially heavy water moving to lighter water) causes magnesium laden water to move through limestone sediments.

Dome (tectonic) A round or elliptical anticlinal upwarp in which the strata dip away in all directions from a high point.

Eolian   Pertaining to or deposited by wind.

Epirogeny   Large scale, regional, primarily vertical movement of the earth's crust.

Extrusive   The venting of molten rocks at the surface. May be by flow (lava) or explosion (ash, volcanic bombs) depending on amount of gas in the magma.

May be from fissures (fractures or joints) or from volcanic vents. Opposite to *intrusive*.

Facies   Picture a barrier beach with a lagoon on one side and ocean on the other. Sediments deposited in each environment are considered a facies of laterally deposited sediments. E.g. Beach facies, Lagoon facies, etc.

Fault   A planar fracture in the earth's crust across which there has been relative displacement of the two blocks parallel to the fracture. **Dip-slip or normal fault:** One side slips down the plane of the fault relative to the other. **Strike-slip fault**: One side slips lateral (horizontal) relative to the other. **Reverse fault**: One side is pushed up the plane of the fault relative to the other. Angle of the fault is usually greater than 45 degrees. **Thrust fault**: One side is pushed over the other. Angle of the fault will be less than 45 degrees and may be very shallow, even horizontal.

Fault block mountains A mountain or range formed when the crust is broken into blocks of different elevations by faulting.

Flysch Facies Muds and sands deposited in deep water (usually over 1,000 feet).

Fold   Bent or warped bedding or sequence of beds that was originally horizontal, or nearly so, and was subsequently deformed.

Formation   The fundamental unit in rock stratigraphic classification. It is a set of rocks (1) that is or once was nearly continuous horizontally, (2) shares some distinctive features of lithology, and (3) is widespread and thick enough to be mapped.

Glass (volcanic) A rock formed when magma or molten rock is cooled too rapidly to allow crystal growth. May form the matrix of an ignimbrite (welded tuff). Obsidian is a volcanic glass.

Group   A series of two or more formations.

Hogback   A ridge formed by the slower erosion of steeply dipping hard strata.

Hoodoos   Weathered vertical spires. On cooling very hot lava or ignimbrites develop a natural vertical hexagonal jointing. On weathering the joints are enlarged and rounded resulting in a field of spires called hoodoos.

Hydrothermal Literally, hot water. Mineral deposits are carried upward from magmas by hot gaseous waters and the minerals are deposited when the gas is released and/or the water cools.

Igneous Rocks	Acidic	Intermediate	Basic
	Cooler magmas		Hotter magmas
	Felsic silicic		Mafic
	Increasing iron and magnesium⇒		
	Decreasing silica⇒		
Extrusive and fine-grained intrusive rocks			
	rhyolite trachyte **dacite**	**andesite**	**basalt**
Intrusive - course grained rocks			

	Granite
	     granodiorite
	               syenite
		diorite	**gabbro**
			anorthosite

Ignimbrite   See *Tuff, Welded Tuff.*

Intermontane Situated between or surrounded by mountains.

Intrusive   The forced emplacement of molten rock between layers of rock or along fractures or faults. Intrusive rocks solidify below the earth's surface. Opposite to *extrusive*.

Joint   Naturally occurring vertical or near vertical crack in rocks.

Laccolith   A concordant, intrusive body that has spread laterally between rock layers and developed a lens shape that domes the overlying rocks.

Lahar   A *mudflow* of unconsolidated volcanic ash, dust, breccia and boulder, that occurs when pyroclastic deposits mix with rain or the water from a lake or melting glacier and flow down the sides of a volcano, sometimes for many miles and with catastrophic effect.

m.y. or Ma   Age of rock in millions of years before present.

Magma   Molten rock that forms igneous rocks upon cooling.

Magma chamber Heat rising in the crust carries molten rock or melts preexisting rock to form a cauldron that feeds magma to intrusive or extrusive emanations.

Mesozoic   Geologic era from 245 to 65 m.y. Geologic periods within this era

Periods	Begins
Cretaceous	146 m.y.
Jurassic	208 m.y.
Triassic	245 m.y.

Mudflow   Explosive volcanoes blow ash and rocks (volcanic bombs) into the air. These pyroclastic rocks settle on the high slopes. During the next heavy rain the ash turns to mud and the accumulated rock debris and mud will flow down the slope and into the surrounding lowland. The flow is called a **lahar** and the resulting deposit a laharic breccia. A mudflow can be catastrophic. In 1985 a mudflow in Columbia killed 22,000 people.

Neogene   Please see *Tertiary*.

Normal fault Vertical or near-vertical fault where the down-thrown side slips in the direction of dip of the fault.

Nuee Ardente "Hot cloud", this is a very hot cloud of ash flowing laterally from an explosive volcano. The cloud is hot enough to vaporize any living thing in its path. Part of the matrix cools as glass and welds the ash into a hard rock. The rock deposited by a nuee ardente is an *ignimbrite* or *welded tuff*. Please see *Pyroclastic flow*.

Paleozoic   Geologic era from 570 to 245 m.y. Geologic periods within this era:

Period	Begins (m.y.)
Permian	290
Pennsylvanian	323
Mississippian	363
Devonian	409
Silurian	439
Ordovician	510
Cambrian	545

Pegmatite   A vein of extremely course grained granite. May contain economic amounts of rare minerals.

Porphyry   An igneous rock containing megascopic mineral crystals suspended in a finely crystalline matrix. The larger crystals are called **phenocrysts**, and the matrix of smaller crystals is called **groundmass**.

Precambrian Geologic time prior to 545 m.y.

| Proterozoic | Geologic time 2500 to 545 m.y. |
| Archeozoic | Geologic time 4600 to 2500 m.y. |

Provenance   Place of origin. Refers to the source of rock particles found in sediments.

Pyroclast Fragment of volcanic material ejected during an eruption.

Pyroclastic flow A hot glowing cloud of volcanic ash, fragments of volcanic rock, ash and gases that pours down the slope of a volcano during an eruption at 60 to 100 miles per hour. It will incinerate every living thing in its path.

Quaternary Geologic period from 1.8 m.y. to Present. Epochs within this period:

Epochs	Begins
Holocene	13,000 years ago
Pleistocene	1.8 m.y. ago

Reverse fault Steeply dipping (>45 degrees) fault where the upthrown side is pushed up over the downthrown side.

Rift, Rift valley A fault bounded trough formed by tension (stretching) of the earth's crust. The Upper Arkansas rift valley is an example.

Rockslide The mass movement of large blocks of detached bedrock sliding more or less as a unit.

Sabkha In desert areas it is an area of evaporation landward from a barrier beach. It is an area of gypsum and salt deposition with some sand.

Shield Volcano A large volcano shaped like a flattened dome and built up almost entirely of numerous flows of lava and welded tuff. The slopes of shield volcanoes seldom exceed 10 degrees.

Sill (intrusive) Igneous rocks intruded sheet-like, parallel to the bedding of the intruded rocks.

Stock (intrusive) An intrusion with the characteristics of a batholith, but less that 100 km2 in area.

Strata Layers of sedimentary rock.

Stratigraphy The science of description, correlation, and classification of sedimentary rocks. Includes the interpretation of sedimentary environments of those strata.

Strike The geographic direction of a line formed by the intersection of a horizontal plane and the plane of tilted or vertical features, such as the bedding of sediment, igneous dikes, fault planes, etc

Syncline A fold in rocks in which the strata dip inward from both sides; a down fold. The opposite of *anticline.*

Synclinorium a series of parallel folds that overall have a down-folded shape.

Tectonics. Pertaining to or designating the rock structure resulting from deformation of the earth's crust.

Tertiary. Geologic period from 65 to 1.8 million years ago. Epochs within this period:

Epoch	Begins (m.y. ago)	
Pliocene	5	] Neogene
Miocene	24	] "
Oligocene	32.7	[Paleogene
Eocene	57	["
Paleocene	65	["

Thrust fault Shallow angle reverse fault (>45 degrees) **Overthrust fault**: Very shallow angle fault where the upthrown side travels some distance laterally over the down thrown side.

Thrust sheet Rocks above an overthrust fault.

Tuff Consolidated volcanic ash.

Turbidite A sedimentary rock deposited by a turbidity current. Graded bedding is characteristic.

Turbidity Current as used here, a down-slope movement of dense, sediment-laden (mud, silt, and sand) water created when the sediment is dislodged and thrown into suspension. Marine turbidity currents laden with suspended sediment move rapidly from the continent shelf, down slopes (usually fed through submarine canyons) and spread out over the abyssal floor.

Volcanic neck The solidified material filling the vent of a dead volcano.

Volcanic bombs. Blobs of lava blown out of an explosive volcano that harden to lava boulders as it falls.

Unconformities

    Erosional unconformity or disconformity Break or gap in the geologic record. Usually a period of non-deposition and erosion. May apply to missing section in a sedimentary sequence.

    Low angle unconformity. Broad regional break where underlying formations are slightly tilted and eroded. Example: Base of Devonian Woodford Shale.

210

Angular Unconformity Erosional surface on folded and faulted strata. Example: Permian Lower Wolfcamp angular unconformity over Central Basin Platform.

Non-conformity Applied to a large break in the record where igneous or metamorphic rocks are overlain by much younger sedimentary rocks. Example: Base of Cambrian Hickory Sandstone over the Llano Uplift.

Uplift Refers to the epierogenic or local raising of the earth's crust by tectonic forces.

Welded tuff Deposits of volcanic ash that flowed in a cloud away from a volcano. When very hot at time of flow (nuee ardente), some of the ash particles will fuse as glass and thus weld the ash to a hard resistant rock (ignimbrite).

Xenoliths Masses of country (surrounding) rock included in an intrusive rock mass

Brick red baked interval in volcanic ash below a lava. Road cut is in Davis Mountains along State Highway 118 on the south flank of Mount Locke.